So you really want to learn

Science

Book 2

Answer Book

Published by Galore Park Publishing Ltd
19/21 Sayers Lane
Tenterden, Kent TN30 6BW

www.galorepark.co.uk

Text copyright © W. R. Pickering 2005
Illustrations copyright © Galore Park 2005
Illustrations by Graham Edwards

Typography and layout by Typetechnique, London W1
Printed by Charlesworth Press, Wakefield

ISBN: 978 1 902984 38 4

First published 2005, reprinted 2006, 2007, 2008, 2010, 2011

Details of other Galore Park publications are available at www.galorepark.co.uk

ISEB Revision Guides, publications and examination papers may also be obtained from Galore Park.

So you really want to learn

Science

Book 2

Answer Book

By W. R Pickering B.Sc., PhD., M.I.Biol., C.Biol., F.L.S

Edited by Louise Martine B.Sc. (Lon)

GALORE PARK

www.galorepark.co.uk

Acknowledgements

The publishers would like to thank David Penter and Richard Balding for their help during the production of this book. We are most grateful.

Important Note for Teachers: Update in Energy Terminology

The revised syllabus for 2008 refers to 'internal thermal energy'. It is no longer desirable to use 'heat' as a noun or adjective as in the term 'heat energy'. Strictly, the energy that an object has due to its temperature should be called its 'internal energy'. When an object is heated, 'thermal energy' flows into it thus increasing its 'internal energy'. So the **flow** of what used to be called 'heat energy' should be called 'thermal energy' and how much it actually has should be called its 'internal energy'. However, we consider this distinction between internal and thermal energy an unnecessary complication at this level. In *So you really want to learn Science Book 2* the term 'internal/thermal energy' has been used to indicate that either adjective is acceptable. This has been shortened to 'thermal energy' where the use of the full term would be awkward (in labelling some diagrams and where the term is used several times in a paragraph).

The energy stored by an object that has been bent, stretched or compressed has been described as 'elastic/strain (potential) energy' as either 'elastic' or 'strain' is acceptable and 'potential' is optional.

Tom Adams (Team Leader, ISEB Physics Panel)

Items that affect this Answer Book are that the following are no longer examined at Common Entrance:

1. Conduction, Convection and Radiation (Exercise 23.2 Conduction and Convection).

2. Thermal energy flowing from a body at one temperature to a body at a lower temperature (Exercise 23.3 Radiation).

Contents

Chapter 9

Chapter 10

Materials and their properties

Chapter 11

Chapter 12

Chapter 13

Chapter 14

Chapter 15

Chapter 16

Chapter 17

Physical processes

Chapter 18

Chapter 19

Chapter 20

Chapter 21

Chapter 22

Introduction

This answer book together with the Pupils' Book and the Teacher's Resource CD has been designed to help teachers and parents to prepare pupils for KS3 Science and the 13+ Common Entrance Examinations.

This answer book contains:

- **A suggested programme of study**
- **A complete set of answers to the questions laid out in Science Book 2**

It should be emphasised that for some questions there are alternative answers, and teachers should be prepared to be flexible!

Suggested programme of study

There is a required content coverage for science to 13+, determined by the Independent Schools Examination Board (ISEB). The specification for the Common Entrance (CE) Examination at 13+ closely follows the specification laid down by the Qualifications and Curriculum Authority (QCA) for science at Key Stage 3. This is designed to ensure comparability between the two schemes and allowing flexibility of movement between the maintained and independent sector.

Science Book 2 exactly follows the specification of the ISEB. The content is organised into three sections, Life and living processes, Materials and their properties and Physical processes. Opportunities to develop Sc1 skills in scientific enquiry are distributed throughout all three sections. It is not expected that the content would necessarily be covered in this sequence.

The QCA also suggests a programme of study for delivery of the content of the specification and for the development of the skills required by this stage of a young person's education in science. The following table indicates the QCA scheme and how it may be implemented using this book. There is no compulsion, of course to follow this scheme. Many schools may choose to deliver the content and skills training within their own programmes of study, this table represents just one possible scheme.

KS3 unit	QCA unit title	Science Book 2
7A	Cells	**Chapter 1:** Living organisms are made of cells
7B	Reproduction	**Chapter 4:** Reproduction; The Menstrual Cycle; Pregnancy and the placenta
7C	Environment and feeding relationships	**Chapter 9:** Feeding relationships; Food chains and pollution; **Chapter 10:** Conservation
7D	Variation and classification	**Chapter 8:** Variation and classification; Variety of Life
7E	Acids and alkalis	**Chapter 14:** Acids and bases; Acid or alkali – Indicators
7F	Simple chemical reactions	**Chapter 16:** Chemical Reactions; Useful chemical tests; Important chemical changes
7G	Particle model of solids, liquids and gases	**Chapter 12:** Physical changes; Solids, liquids or gases
7H	Solutions	**Chapter 13:** Pure substance or mixture?; More about mixtures – solutions and solubility
7I	Energy resources	**Chapter 18:** Energy resources; Renewable energy resources; Fossil fuels **Chapter 24:** Saving energy (energy conservation)

7J	Electrical circuits	**Chapter 20:** Electricity on the move; Series and Parallel Circuits; Problems with circuits
7K	Forces and their effects	**Chapter 26:** Forces and linear motion; Friction and motion; Balanced and unbalanced forces
7L	The solar system and beyond	**Chapter 25:** Earth and the solar system; The Sun and other stars; The year and the seasons
8A	Food and digestion	**Chapter 2:** Balanced diet; Digestion and absorption
8B	Respiration	**Chapter 5:** Respiration; Respiration and breathing; Smoking and disease
8C	Microbes and disease	**Chapter 6:** Microbes and disease; Individuals and the community
8D	Ecological relationships	**Chapter 10:** Adaptation; Conservation; Populations and the community
8E	Atoms and elements	**Chapter 15:** Elements and the Periodic Table; Inside an atom
8F	Compounds and mixtures	**Chapter 13:** Pure substance or mixture; Compounds are made when elements combine; Separating mixtures
8I	Heating and cooling	**Chapter 23:** Temperature and energy; The passage of thermal energy; More methods of thermal energy transfer
8J	Magnets and electromagnets	**Chapter 22:** Magnets and magnetic fields; Electricity and magnetism
8K	Light	**Chapter 28:** Light and light sources; Mirrors and reflection; Refraction of light; Light and colour
8L	Sound and hearing	**Chapter 29:** Vibration and sound; Different sounds
9A	Inheritance and selection	**Chapter 8:** Selective breeding; Variation and classification
9B	Fit and healthy	**Chapter 3:** Functions of the skeleton **Chapter 6:** Healthy Living **Chapter 5:** Smoking and disease
9C	Plants and photosynthesis	**Chapter 7:** Photosynthesis; Leaves and roots help plants to grow
9D	Plants for food	**Chapter 7:** Photosynthesis **Chapter 9:** Feeding relationships

9E	Reactions of metals and metal compounds	**Chapter 15:** Metals and non-metals **Chapter 17:** Reactions of metals; Corrosion; Extraction of metals from ores
9F	Patterns of reactivity	**Chapter 17:** Reactions of metals; Extraction of metals from ores **Chapter 14:** More reactions of acids
9G	Environmental chemistry	**Chapter 16:** Important chemical changes **What is chemistry?:** What is chemistry? **Chapter 18:** Fossil fuels
9H	Using chemistry	**Chapter 16:** Important chemical changes **What is chemistry?:** What is chemistry?
9I	Energy and electricity	**Chapter 19:** Electricity and energy; Generating electricity from fuels **Chapter 18:** Fossil fuels
9J	Gravity and space	**Chapter 25 and 26:** The force of gravity; Keeping planets in orbit
9K	Speeding up	**Chapter 26:** Distance and time
9L	Pressure and moments	**Chapter 27:** Forces and rotation; Force and pressure; Hydraulics
9M	Investigating scientific questions	**Investigations in science:** Carrying out investigations **Chapter 11:** Experiments in Chemistry

Chapter 1

Exercise 1.1: Cells and tissues

1. (a) A = nucleus, B = cytoplasm, C = vacuole, D = (cellulose) cell wall

    (b) We call a group of similar cells with the same function a **tissue**.

    (c) You get a very thin slice of a stem ready for viewing under a microscope by mounting it in water on a slide/stain/cover slip.

    (d) Plant cells are different from typical animal cells in that they have a large vacuole and a cellulose cell wall.

    (e) These cells are different from typical leaf cells because they do not have chloroplasts.

2.

Cell	Function	Process
White blood cell	Traps microbes	To prevent disease
Leaf cell	Absorbs light	For photosynthesis
Cell in intestine	Produces enzymes	To digest food
Red blood cell	Transports oxygen	For respiration

3. (a) Chloroplasts are present in leaf cells but not in root cells.

    (b) The cell wall and chloroplasts cannot be found in animal cells.

    (c)

Function	Part of the Cell
Photosynthesis takes place here.	Chloroplast
It controls the cell's activities.	Nucleus
It helps to keep the shape of the cell.	Cell wall
It controls substances entering and leaving the cell.	Cell membrane

Chapter 2

Exercise 2.1: A balanced diet

1. As well as water, a balanced diet should contain **fats, carbohydrates, proteins, vitamins, minerals** and **fibre**.

2. Fish: A good food for body-builders

    Butter: A dairy product that can supply energy and some vitamins.

    Spaghetti: A main source of energy.

    Milk: An excellent source of vitamins and minerals – an ideal baby food and can provide a lot of our water needs.

    Wholemeal bread: Helps prevent constipation.

    Lettuce: Helps prevent constipation / can provide a lot of our water needs.

3. (a) (i) water   (ii) skin

    (b) 200g of chips: **18 mg**; 200g of potato baked in its skin: **28 mg**

    (c) Not enough calcium – bones

          Not enough fibre – intestine

          Too much fat – heart

Exercise 2.2: Digestion

1.

Enzyme	A molecule that speeds up the digestion of foods
Ingestion	The process of taking food into the gut
Digestion	Breaking food down into small, soluble particles (molecules)
Absorption	Transferring digested food particles into the bloodstream
Egestion	Removing indigestible materials from the gut

2. (a) He might check the temperatures in the different parts of the experiment with a **thermometer**.

    (b)   **A graph to show the effects of temperature on the action of an enzyme**

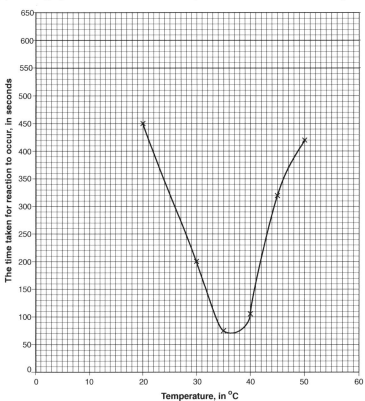

    (c)   The best temperature for the enzyme-controlled reaction to occur is **35 °C**.

    (d)   Human body temperature is **37 °C**. Using the graph the reaction would take approximately **80 seconds** at human body temperature.

    (e)   It would take **approx 540 seconds** for the reaction to occur at 60 °C.

    (f)   For Felix to make sure that this experiment was a fair test he would keep have to keep all other variables constant.

Extension question

3. (a) They could test the mixture using iodine solution. The iodine would turn blue-black if starch was present at the start of the experiment.

    (b)   The best temperature to keep the mixture at while this breakdown was going on would be **37 °C**.

    (c)   To prove that starch has not crossed the wall of the gut into the water Felix might **test the surrounding solution for starch by using iodine**.

    (d)   Starch **molecules are too large** to cross through the gut membrane.

    (e)   The water in the beaker represents **the blood in the body**.

Chapter 3

Exercise 3.1: Skeleton and movement

1.

The skeleton	Has joints for movement/supports the softer tissues of the body
Blood cells	Are made inside some bones
Bone	Is one of the hardest tissues in the body
Calcium	Is an essential mineral for strong bones
Tendons	Connect muscle to bone
Ligaments	Connect bone to bone
The skull	Protects the brain
The ribs	Protect the heart and lungs
A synovial joint	Makes its own lubricating fluid
Cartilage	Reduces friction between the bones

2. (a) The leg bones are stronger than the arm bones in humans because **they have more weight to bear**.

(b) Pregnant women should drink a lot of milk in order to **make their baby's bones**.

(c) X-rays can be used to check for broken bones because **bones are dense**.

(d) Scooter riders have to wear crash helmets by law since they **offer extra protection for the brain**.

(e) Cartilage is essential in the knee joints so as to **prevent the wear at the ends of the bone**.

3. The biceps **contracts,** thus becoming **shorter and fatter**. The triceps muscle is the **antagonistic** muscle to the biceps and so it **relaxes** and becomes **longer and thinner**. If you straighten your arm, the **opposite** happens.

Chapter 4

Exercise 4.1: The reproductive systems

1. A = Seminal vesicle; B = Prostate gland; C = Sperm duct; D = Urethra;
   E = Testis/testicle; F = Scrotum/scrotal sac; G = Penis

2. A = Oviduct/fallopian tube; B = Ovary; C = Muscular wall of the uterus; D = Cervix;
   E = Vagina; F = Opening of vagina

3.

Testes	Produce the sperm and the male sex hormone
Sperm	The male gamete
Semen	A fluid for the sperm to swim in
Scrotum	Hold the testes outside the body
Sperm duct	Carries sperm from testes to the penis
Penis	Delivers sperm in semen to the vagina
Prostate gland	Produces a fluid for sperm to swim in

4.

Ovaries	Produce the female gametes
Egg	The female gamete
Oviducts	Carry eggs from ovaries to uterus
Vagina	The birth canal
Womb	The place where the baby develops
Cervix	Where the sperm are released when the male ejaculates

5. The sperm is different from the egg because it has to move, whereas the egg is designed to contain food. They are similar in that each has a half set of chromosomes.

Exercise 4.2: Menstruation and fertilisation

1.

Ovulation	The release of a mature female gamete
Ejaculation	The release of sperm in the semen
Menstruation	The breakdown and release of the inner wall of the uterus
Fertilisation	Egg and sperm joining together
Conception	The time when a fertilized egg 'sticks' to the wall of the uterus
Copulation	Sexual intercourse

Exercise 4.3: Placenta and birth

1 (a) An expectant mother knows when she is about to give birth because her **uterus** begins to experience waves of contraction. Eventually the contractions are so powerful that the **cervix** dilates, the **amniotic sac** bursts and the waters are released.

   (b) Further powerful contractions push the baby through the **vagina** or birth canal. Once the baby has been delivered, it is important that it takes deep breaths because it may have been deprived of **oxygen** as the **umbilical** cord is compressed during delivery. This cord is clamped and cut, and gentle contractions of the uterus cause the **placenta** to come away from the wall of the uterus and pass out of the vagina as the **afterbirth**.

2. (a) Left hand diagram: A = Placenta; B = Umbilical cord; C = Embryo; D = Wall of uterus; E = Amniotic fluid; F = Amniotic sac; G = Vagina

   (b) Right hand diagram: A = Placenta; B = Umbilical cord; D = Wall of uterus; E = Amniotic fluid; F = Fetus; G = Cervix; H = Amniotic sac

Extension question

3. **Gestation period**

    (a) **A scatter graph to show whether there is a correlation between the mass of an adult animal and its gestation period**

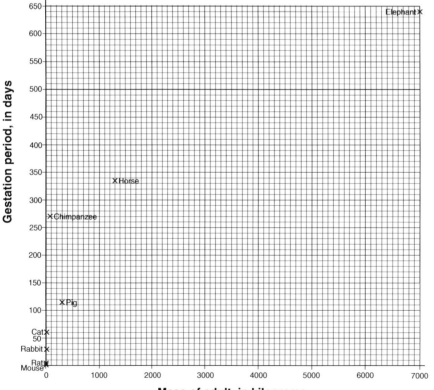

(b) (i)   Check pupils' answers. They could compare for example rabbit (1.5kg with 4-10 young), with cat (4kg with 3 to 5 young).

(ii) Check pupils' answers. They could compare for example rabbit (30 days with 3 litters of 4-10) with cat (60 days with litters of 3-5).

(c) (i)   About 20 days

(ii) About 35 days

(iii) About 250 days

Note: This is a difficult exercise because of the graph scale. Some pupils may recognise it is better to draw a second graph with a different scale on the x-axis to obtain a more accurate estimate of gestation period in small mammals.

Chapter 5

Exercise 5.1 : Respiration

1.   (a)   glucose + oxygen → carbon dioxide + water + energy

   (b)   (i)   1220 − (700+180+140) = 200 kJ

   Percentage = 200/1220 = 16.4%

   (ii)   The energy is used for **movement, growth, maintaining body temperature, reproduction and cell division**.

2.   (a)   For a safe experiment Felix must have the open end of tube **pointing away from him**.

   (b)   For a fair test Felix must use the **same mass of crisp**; the **same volume of water**; and the **same measuring position of apparatus**.

   (c)   (i)   The change in the temperature of the water will be greater. This is because more energy is released so there will be a greater increase in temperature.

   (d)   (i)   Since fibre cannot be digested its energy content cannot be released

   (ii)   Crispbread is preferential to potato crisps because it has more protein, less fat and more fibre.

Exercise 5.2 : Breathing

1.   Air sac – bronchiole – bronchus – trachea

2.   (a)   Cartilage prevents the collapse of the trachea during breathing in.

   (b)   (i)   A = carbon dioxide; b = oxygen

   (ii)   It is easy for gases to pass across the wall of an air sac because the **wall is very thin and it has a large surface area**.

3.   (a)   Breathing involves moving air in and out of the lungs whereas respiration involves the release of energy from food.

   (b)   Breathing is important because it replaces oxygen and removes carbon dioxide.

   (c)   Respiration releases energy from digested food. Energy is needed for life processes.

   (d)   Look for release of carbon dioxide (limewater turns milky); look for release of energy (as thermal energy), look for the consumption (uptake) of oxygen.

4.   (a)   500 cm^3

   (b)   Air breathed in has more oxygen, less carbon dioxide and, usually, less water vapour than air breathed out.

   (c)   Carbon dioxide, water vapour and thermal energy.

Extension question

5. (a) **A graph to show the changes in breathing rate over the time period of this investigation**

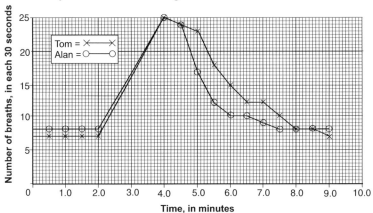

(b) Alan is the fitter since he needed fewer breathes for exercise and his recovery was faster.

Exercise 5.3: Smoking

1. (a) The function of a ciliated cell is to move mucus up from the lungs.

(b) Substances in cigarette smoke cause the cilia to stop moving.

(c) Nicotine causes the addiction to smoking.

2. (a) 1950 – 55

(b) **Tar** causes lung cancer.

(c) Smoking increases the chances of developing heart disease, by **reducing the transport of oxygen to working heart muscle**.

Extension question

3. (a) 45%

(b) Pupils may have drawn either a bar chart or a pie chart.

A pie chart to show the causes of death of cigarette smokers in Great Britain

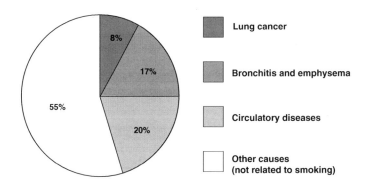

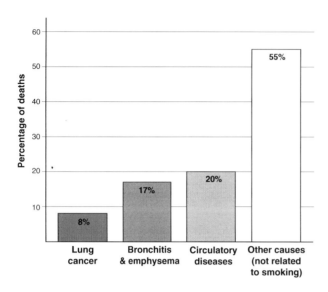

A bar chart to show the causes of death of cigarette smokers in Great Britain

Whilst a bar chart and a pie chart both have values as proportions of the whole, the pie chart presents all the data within one total area and thus it makes comparisons of the categories easier to see.

(c) (i) Emphysema is a disease caused by smoking. In normal lungs, lung tissue has thinner walls and a greater surface area. In the lungs of a person with emphysema the tissue walls between the air sacs will have been destroyed. This means there is less surface area for gas exchange.

(ii) The supply of oxygen to the blood in the person with emphysema will be reduced because the area over which gas exchange can take place is very much reduced.

(iii) Other diseases caused by smoking include: **cancer**, which results in much pain and can ultimately lead to death; **bronchitis**, which results in coughing; **heart and arterial disease**, patients could suffer heart attacks, raised blood pressure.

Chapter 6

Exercise 6.1: Healthy living

1.   Three requirements for a healthy lifestyle include:
   - a balanced diet – especially limiting the consumption of fat;
   - no health risks – not smoking, not taking drugs and limiting alcohol consumption; and
   - regular exercise.

2.   It is difficult to give up smoking because the nicotine in the tobacco causes addiction.

3.   Three benefits of regular exercise could include **strength, stamina, weight control** and **fitness of the heart and arteriol systems**.

4.

Smoking	Lung cancer
Excessive use of alcohol	Damage to the liver
Addiction to drugs	Poor brain development
Over-eating of fatty foods	Obesity
Too little exercise	Weakness of muscles
Breathing aerosols	Choking to death

Extension questions

5.   (a)   **A graph to show a pupil's heart rate measured every five minutes for a period of an hour**

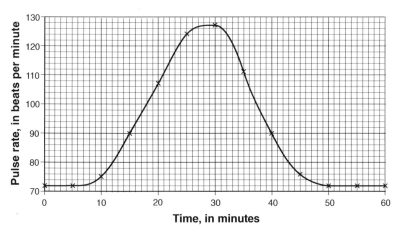

    (b)   (i)   The resting heart rate   **72 BPM**

            (ii)   When the pupil began to take exercise   **after 7 minutes**

            (iii)   When the pupil stopped exercising   **30 minutes**

            (iv)   How long the pupil's pulse took to return to normal   **20 minutes**

(c) The pulse rate increased during exercise because more blood (glucose/oxygen) was being delivered to working muscles so that respiration (energy release) could go on and the muscles could work harder.

6. Check pupils' investigations into the health problems caused by the overuse of alcohol. They may identify the short term affects such as drunkenness and the long term effects on various parts of the body such as the brain or liver.

Exercise 6.2: Microbes and disease

1. (a) Any suitable virus infection e.g. common cold, influenza, HIV, chicken pox, mumps, polio, small pox. Any appropriate example is acceptable.

   (b) Infectious: e.g. common cold, influenza etc… Any appropriate example is acceptable

   (c) Poor diet: e.g. anaemia, rickets, scurvy. Any appropriate example is acceptable.

   (d) Bacterial infection e.g. tuberculosis, food poisoning (Salmonella), cholera, pneumonia, typhoid, blood poisoning, whooping cough etc… Any appropriate example is acceptable.

   (e) Unhealthy lifestyle: Heart disease, lung cancer, cholera, AIDS etc… Any appropriate example is acceptable.

2. Red soldiers = red blood cells/platelets (involved in blood clotting); white soldiers = white blood cells (involved in destroying microbes). Yes she was correct.

3. **Bacteria** have cytoplasm, are bigger than viruses, have cell walls and can live inside or outside the host. Bacteria can be killed by antibiotics, antiseptics or disinfectants.

   Viruses only come alive when they enter the body, they have a simple structure, a few genes wrapped in a protein coat. Viruses cannot be controlled by antibiotics.

4. An antibiotic is a chemical made by a fungus that kills bacteria.

   An antibiotic works inside the body. An antiseptic works outside the body e.g. on the skin. Disinfectant kills microbes on surfaces or in drains but not on or in the body because it would be too strong.

Extension question

5. (a) James Phipps would have caught smallpox.

   (b) Check pupils' answers. Look for understanding of antibody production. They need to have shown that contact with cowpox generated antibodies in James Phipps and that the antibodies then recognised and dealt with the antigens / the smallpox virus.

   (c) Check pupils' investigations into why people are no longer vaccinated against smallpox.

Chapter 7

Exercise 7.1: Photosynthesis

1. The ethanol turns green because the green pigment, **chlorophyll, is soluble in ethanol**.

2. (a) The pupils should describe the process of photosynthesis. Plants make their food (glucose) by combining carbon dioxide gas from the air with water and nutrients from the soil. The energy they need to do this comes form the sunlight. The energy in the sunlight is trapped by a green pigment, called chlorophyll, contained in chloroplasts, in the cells of the leaves of the plant. This process is called photosynthesis and it provides food for the plant.

    (b) You could test to show that starch has been stored in the bulb using **iodine solution**. The starch will be coloured blue-black by the iodine.

    (b) Bluebells grow in the Spring, before most trees have their leaves. As a result they do not compete with trees for light and can photosynthesise, grow and flower before they are shaded by the trees.

3. (a)   **A graph to show the effect of light intensity on the volume of oxygen released**

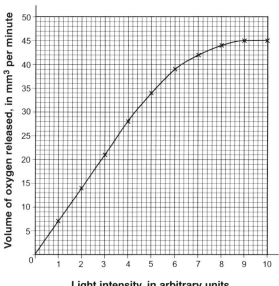

    (b) 3.5 units

    (c) 9 units. The information indicates that it would be a waste of energy to provide a light intensity of more than 9 units.

4.

Factor to be varied	Factor to be measured	Factors to be kept constant
Light	Length of plant	Carbon dioxide, water, temperature
Amount of carbon dioxide	Length of plant	Light, water, temperature
Amount of water	Length of plant	Light, carbon dioxide, temperature
Temperature	Length of plant	Light, carbon dioxide, water

Exercise 7.2: Plant nutrition

1. Two jobs carried out by the stem of a plant could include:
    - holding leaves up for photosynthesis;
    - holding up flowers for pollination;
    - transporting water and nutrients around the plant.

2. The leaf's job is to **absorb light for photosynthesis**. It is well adapted for this job because it is:
    - thin
    - contains cholophyll
    - has a large surface area
    - has pores (stomata)

3. (a) (i) Only a small amount of the water reaches the roots of the trees since:
          - much of the water evaporates from the soil surface in the heat of the sun; or
          - the water does not soak into the tightly compacted soil.

    (ii) Mango trees do not grow well in soil, which is hard and tightly packed, because it is too **difficult for roots and water to penetrate** and there is **not much oxygen in the soil** for respiration of roots.

    (b) Trees need water for:
         - photosynthsesis;
         - helping the plant retain its rigidity and this supports its stems and leaves;
         - transporting dissolved substances through their bodies.

    (c) (i) Pieces of rock are placed in the trenches under the pipes so that the water can flow more easily and can be reached by the tree roots more effectively.
        (ii) Plants need nitrates to make proteins, this helps the plants to grow properly.

4. (a) (i) Light is needed by plants to provide the energy needed for photosynthesis to take place.
        (ii) The Tillandsia grows on the high branches because in the dense rainforests the lower branches would be shaded. The light intensity would be too low for photosynthesis. The high branches will be exposed to greater amounts of light.

    (b) Most plants absorb **water** and **minerals** through their root hairs.

    (c) B

Extension question

5. (a)

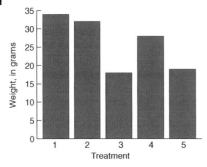

    (b) The reduction of light to only half of the 'ideal' amount had the greatest effect on the plants' growth.

    (c) This treatment affected the plants in this way because light is needed for photosynthesis. If the plant cannot photosynthesise efficiently, the plant will not have enough food and energy to grow properly.

Chapter 8

Exercise 8.1: Variation

1.

Gene	A chemical that controls a characteristic of an organism
Chromosome	A thin strand, found in the nucleus, that carries a set of genes
Variation	The differences between organisms
Environment	All factors affecting an organism
Zygote	The first cell that contains genes from two parents
Fertilisation	A process that joins sex cells together

2. (a) Variation occurs in two forms. **Discontinuous** which shows clear cut separation between groups, and **continuous** variation of groups, which almost run into each other. The first of these is the result of **genes** alone, whilst the second is also affected by **environmental** factors.

    (b) The genes inherited by an organism come from its **parents**. One set comes from the **mother** and one set from the **father**. The overall appearance of an organism can be explained in a simple equation: **genotype (genes)** plus **effects of environment** equals **phenotype (appearance).**

3. One's **blood group** is an example of discontinuous variation.

    (a) A person's blood group is the only example for which there are clear-cut groups. E.g. A, B, AB or O.

    (b) Body mass, chest circumference and height are all quantitative and any individual may have any value for each of these within a wide range. Hairstyle is rejected because it can easily be altered and so belongs to no fixed category.

Extension question

4. (a) **A bar chart to investigate the heights of pupils in the first year of secondary school**

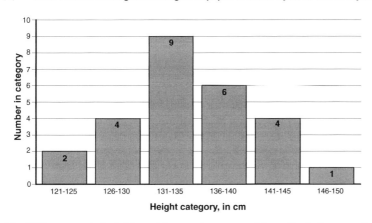

    (b) Differences in height could occur because of the effect of genes (e.g. two tall parents) or the environment (e.g. diet).

    (c) Check pupils' answers but gender is the most obvious.

Exercise 8.2: The variety of life

1.

Feature	Fish	Amphibian	Reptile	Bird	Mammal
Backbone	+	+	+	+	+
Scales	+	–	+	–	–
Feathers	–	–	–	+	–
Hairy skin	–	–	–	–	+

2.

Has wings, a constant body temperature and lays eggs with hard shells	Bird
Has no backbone, two body parts and eight jointed legs	Spider
Has a body made of a single cell with a clear nucleus and cytoplasm	Protist
Has no backbone, three body parts and six jointed legs	Insect
Has cells with a definite cell wall but does not feed by photosynthesis	Fungus
Has hair, provides milk for its young and has a constant body temperature	Mammal
Has a backbone, gills, fins and scales	Fish
Has flowers for reproduction, green leaves	Flowering plant

Extension question

3. (a)

Latin name	Common name
Fraxinus excelsior	**Beech**
Quercus robur	English oak
Pan troglodytes	**Chimpanzee**
Loxodonta africana	**African elephant**
Digitalis purpurea	Foxglove
Rana temporaria	Common frog

(b) A common system of names enables communication between scientists from different countries.

(c) French = LION; German = LOWE Swahili = SIMBA

Exercise 8.3: Adaptation

1. Small birds that eat insects migrate south for the winter because the cold weather kills many of the insects that provide their food supply. They must fly to a warmer area further south where there is a better food supply. Examples: swift, swallow, house martin, sand martin, any warbler or any other valid example.

2. A caterpillar can avoid being eaten by a bird by being camouflaged, by appearing larger (hairs) or more frightening (markings) than it really is. It maybe coloured in a way that makes it appear poisonous.

3. Daffodils are adapted to survive winter conditions because their underground bulbs have stores of food. When the leaves and stem die back the food reserves in the bulbs are not damaged.

4. Hedgehog, squirrel, dormouse all hibernate so as to avoid using up energy at times of the year when food is scarce, and when the low air temperature makes it difficult for them to regulate their body temperature.

Extension questions

5. Check the pupils' answers. Look for references and that they have given a suitable description related to the Sun/Earth's magnetic field.

6. Check the pupils' answers. Look for examples of migrations in other species of insects, birds, marine mammals, and large herbivorous mammals. Many birds and a few **bats** of cold and temperate regions migrate to warmer areas during the winter. Herbivores of cold regions, such as elk, caribou and moose have summer and winter ranges; many herbivores of warm regions, such as the African antelopes, migrate seasonally to avoid drought.

    In many cases migration provides a suitable place for reproduction, which may not be the place most suitable for the feeding and other daily activities of adults. For example hundreds of thousands of gnus (wildebeests) of E Africa take part in annual migrations to calving grounds. Many fishes migrate to spawning grounds, and in some cases this involves a change from saltwater to freshwater (e.g., salmon) or vice versa (e.g., freshwater eels). Sea turtles, seals, and many sea birds come ashore to breed, and most amphibians gather near water at the breeding season. Fur seals and many whales make ocean voyages of thousands of miles to their breeding grounds, the former coming ashore on islands.

Chapter 9

Exercise 9.1: Food chains

1. Check the pupils' answers. Check that the food chain starts with a producer and goes on through herbivores and carnivores; an example could be:

    Primrose – caterpillar – small bird.

2. Herbivore: caterpillar, rabbit, slug, snail.

    Carnivore: fox, thrush, black bird, bat.

    Omnivore: badger.

    Decomposer = fungus/mushroom. Decomposers are important because they break down dead organisms. This put minerals back into the soil again.

3.

Sparrow hawk 1

Blue tits 25

Worms 2,500

Leaves 25,000

Extension question

4. (a) Check pupils' answers. One example of a food web could be:

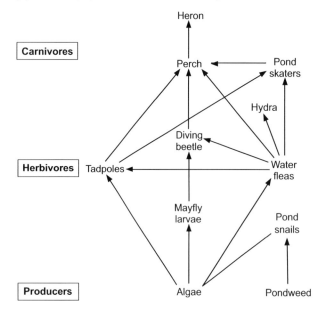

(b)   Herons.

(c)   Animals and plants that die before they are eaten are **decomposed**.

(d)   Check pupils have identified an appropriate food chain and that they have correctly drawn a pyramid of numbers to reflect it.

Exercise 9.2: Food chains and pollution

1.   Farmers use **fertilisers** to increase the yield of their crops. The fertilisers are spread onto the fields and supply several minerals, including **nitrates**, which are needed for plant growth. Sometimes farmers spread too much fertiliser on the fields and when rain falls, **leaching** occurs. The fertilisers are washed into nearby streams and rivers. The fertilisers can then be used by tiny plants called **algae.** This causes them to reproduce very quickly. This makes the water go very **cloudy**, which cuts out the **light** to other plants that are rooted at the bottom of streams and rivers. These rooted plants then die and are **decomposed** by **bacteria**. The bacteria use up all the **oxygen.** This causes many fish and aquatic insects die. The water becomes very smelly and very few organisms can live there. This is an example of **pollution**.

Extension question

2.   (a)   He would use the **filtration** process.

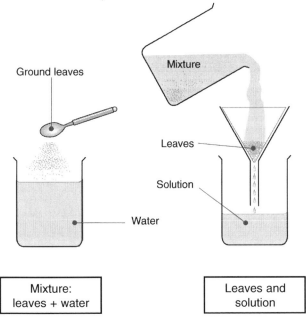

(b)   **Hypothesis**: plant juice can kill insects.

Prediction: more plant juice will kill more insects.

(c)   Input variable: concentration of insecticide.

(d)   Output variable: the number of aphids left alive.

(e)   Yes this was a fair test because all the other variables (same species plant, 100 aphids on each plant, all in the same environment) were kept constant.

(f)   **The effect of the concentration of insecticide on the survivlal of aphids**

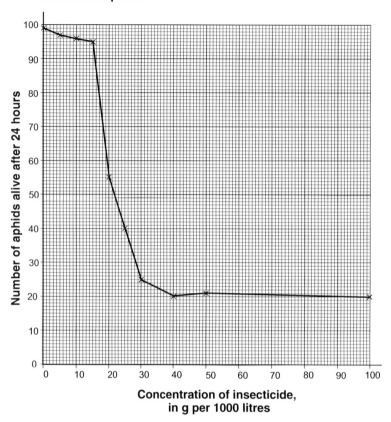

(g)   The concentration of pesticide needed to kill 50% of the aphids 22 – 23 g per 1000 litres.

(h)   Yes the results do support the scientist's prediction, but only up to about 35 ppm.

Chapter 10

Exercise 10.1: Populations

1.	The numbers stopped rising because there could have been:
	–	competition and a resulting shortage of food;
	–	a shortage of predators;
	–	disease.

2.	(a)	The animals will move into the container because it is too hot/too light.

	(b)	(i)	Fungi act as decomposers in the recycling of materials
		(ii)	Arthropods
		(iii)	By jumping a springtail can escape predators and can move to new feeding sites.

3.	(a)	The graph tells us that the number of organisms increases to a certain point and then levels off. It rises slowly at first then more quickly. The population eventually stops increasing.

	(b)	Shortage of food (or some other limiting factor such as predators or disease) could eventually slow down the population growth.

	(c)	Disease, pollution, fire or flood might cause an animal species to fall suddenly in numbers in its natural habitat.

Exercise 10.2: Conservation

1.	Check the results of pupils' investigations into conservation work. Examples could be: the otter, red kite, and most orchids.

2.	Check the results of pupils' investigations into conservation work in zoos. Conservation agendas in zoos could include:
	–	Conservation breeding.
	–	Partnership (with wildlife departments, sharing expertise, training, relocation of animals, governments).
	–	Public education and awareness programmes.
	–	Protection and restoration of habitat and biodiversity.

Extension questions

3.	(a)	5000 miles per year.

	(b)	Reduce the variety of wildlife and increase arable land.

	(c)	Half of the hedges removed in 1968 (i.e. 5000 miles) were replaced in the period between 1980 and 1985 (i.e. 2500 miles per year).

	(d)	Farming is more efficient / much food can be imported cheaply.

	(e)	A, D, E, F, H, I.

4. (a) Timber resources are reduced as trees are cut for paper.

    (b) Recycling means re-using resources; reafforestation means replanting areas from which trees had been removed.

    (c) Any suitable example, e.g. scots pine.
         Any suitable example e.g. oak, beech.

    (d) Coniferous trees grow more quickly so provide rapid income, but have fewer habitats for native species so are not so rich in wildlife.

    (e) Habitats would be covered and so wildlife communities would be destroyed.

Chapter 11

Exercise 11.1: Experiments in chemistry

1. From your measurements you can tell that the same volume of alcohol has less mass than the same volume of water. Alcohol has a lower density than water. Water has a density of 1.0 g/cm^2 and alcohol has a density of 0.8 g/cm^3.

2. $260 - 95 = 165$ g of water can be carried.

3. Briefly describe what each of the following pieces of apparatus is used for:

    (a) Conical flask: Used for mixing solutions, without heating

    (b) Measuring cylinder: Used for measuring the volume of liquids

    (c) Spatula: Used for handling solid chemicals; for example when adding a solid to a liquid.

    (d) Tripod: Used to support apparatus above a Bunsen burner.

    (e) Filter funnel: Used to separate solids from liquids, using filter paper.

    (f) Pipette: Used measure and transfer small volumes of liquid.

4. (a) 1,220 g

    (b) 259 s

    (c) 22 min 0 s

    (d) 2.34 dm^3

    (e) 3.40 kg

    (f) 2984 ml

Extension question

5. Here are some possible answers:

    – Open fire in a lab is a hazard. Use a controlled source of thermal energy, e.g. a bunsen burner.

    – Looking into a vessel (or test tube) when heating something is dangerous. Look in from the side, or heat substances in glass vessels so that the contents are clearly visible.

    – Long beards, hair, ties etc., should be trimmed or tied back.

    – Stockinged feet are dangerous, causing slipping, and breakages of glass etc., Wear sensible shoes in the lab.

    – Spillages should be dealt with safely. Use gloves, a well-soaked cleaning rag and a plastic washing up bowl with plenty of water.

    – Eye protection (goggles) must be used when handling acids and indeed most solutions.

    – Proper space must be allowed between each workstation. This lab is too crowded for safety.

    – Large glass bottles should be stored on lower shelves and not with books.

- Fumes from the cauldron. Work in a fume cupboard where necessary.
- Do not leave objects (e.g. books) lying on the floor, they can be dangerous obstructions.
- Dangers to the skin. Wear gloves and overalls when necessary.
- Do not carry test-tubes of liquid around the laboratory you may cause spillages.

Exercise 11.2: The Bunsen burner

1.   (a) The input variable in this experiment is having either the **hole open** or **closed.**

    (b) The outcome variable in this experiment is the **time taken for the water to boil**.

    (c) (i) the size and shape of the beaker;

       (ii) the starting temperature of the water;

      (iii) the position of the bunsen burner below the beaker;

      (iv) the position of the gas tap (how much flow of gas);

      (v) the volume of water in the beaker.

2.   (a) II and III cannot be compared in a fair test because there are **two variables, the volume of water and the starting temperature**.

    (b) (i) Gena is testing whether an **open or a closed hole** has a greater effect on the time it took for the water to boil.

      (ii) She can conclude that an open hole produces more thermal energy and therefore it takes less time for the water to boil.

    (c) (i) Gena is testing whether the starting temperature effects the time it takes the water to boil.

      (ii) She can conclude that a higher starting temperature reduces the boiling time.

    (d) Gena should compare the results I and V to find the effect of volume of water on the time taken for the water to boil.

Exercise 11.3: Testing

1. Carbon dioxide/sulphur dioxide – turn Litmus solution red.

2. Anhydrous copper sulphate – turns from blue to white if water is present. Cobalt chloride paper turns from blue to pink if water is present.

3. Limewater can be used to test for **carbon dioxide** – this will turn **milky** (chalky) if carbon dioxide is present. The gas **oxygen** will make a glowing splint **relight.** A lighted splint will make the gas **hydrogen** produce a sound like a (**squeaky**) **pop**.

4. Hydrogen carbonate indicator is used by biologists to test for the presence of carbon dioxide.

Chapter 12

Exercise 12.1: Water and the water cycle

1. Pure water boils at **100 °C** and freezes at **0 °C**. A simple chemical test uses cobalt chloride paper to test for the presence of water. The cobalt chloride paper changes from **blue** to **pink**. Seawater is a **mixture** of many different substances. The presence of these impurities **lowers** the freezing point and **raises** the boiling point of water.

2.

Experiment	Factor to change (input variable)	Factor to measure (outcome variable)	Factors to keep constant (controlled variables)
(a)	Speed of blower	Time taken for cloth to change colour	Distance/size of cloth/initial 'wetness' of cloth
(b)	Type of cloth	Time taken for cloth to change colour	Distance/size of cloth/initial 'wetness' of cloth/speed of blower

Extension project

Check pupils' projects. They should have investigated hurricanes particularly the measurements scientists make and some examples of the results they have obtained. (E.g. The 'Hurricane Hunters' WC-130-J are designed to gather position and intensity data over the ocean by flying directly into the storm, often relaying vital information in the turbulent 'eyewall' of the hurricane to forecasters on land. During the flight, scientists use on-board (Doppler) radars in conjunction with land-based (Doppler) radars to scan the hurricanes insides and gathered data to create a three-dimensional picture of its winds. Pressure and wind speed data are collected.)

Exercise 12.2: Other solids, liquids and gases

1. Wood – Solid
   Carbon dioxide – Gas
   Snow – Solid
   Plastic – Solid
   Salt – Solid
   Vinegar – Liquid
   Stone – Solid
   Lime juice – Liquid
   Water vapour – Gas
   Tomato ketchup – Liquid

2. (a)

Does it...?	Solid	Liquid	Gas
Melt	Yes		
Freeze		Yes	
Boil		Yes	
Compress		Yes	Yes
Conduct thermal energy	Yes		
Expand	Yes	Yes	Yes
Diffuse		Yes	Yes
Stretch	Yes		
Flow		Yes	Yes

(b) Solid – high; Liquid – medium; Gas – low.

Extension questions

3. (a) Magnesium, aluminium, zinc, tin, iron, nickel, copper, silver, lead.

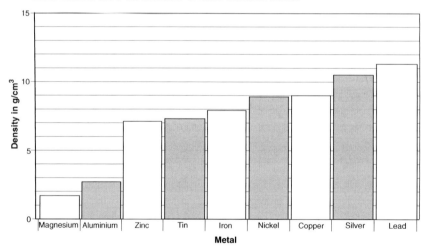

A bar chart to show the densities of some common metals

(b) (i)   Lead has a high density which means that a relatively small volume has a large mass that will weigh the diver down to enable him/her to walk on the sea bed and also, help the diver stay upright. Lead is also cheaper than silver!

(ii) Aluminium is less dense than iron so poles made of aluminium would be much lighter to carry than ones of the same size that had been made of iron.

(iii) Zinc is much (over 15 times), cheaper than tin.

(iv) Aluminium is about three times less dense than copper, so cables of aluminium would be three times lighter than those of the same size that had been made of copper. They are better for hanging between pylons.

(v) Tin has a low melting point (232 °C) and is expensive.

(vi) The densities of both magnesium and aluminium are much lower than the densities of iron and lead. This means that wheels made from a mixture of magnesium and aluminium, would be much lighter than those of the same size, made from a mixture of iron and lead. It is therefore easier to move for acceleration and steering.

4. (a) $D = M/V$

So, $D = \dfrac{975\,g}{10\,000\,cm^3}$

$D = 0.0975\ g/cm^3$

Encourage pupils to keep to the 'three line' layout with the 'equals' signs in line. It is important to try and develop the idea of establishing the correct method when doing calculations, i.e. state the equation – re-arrange if needed – put in the figures – calculate – answer.

(b) $D = M/V$

So, $M = D \times V$

So, $M = 9.0\ g/cm^3 \times 27\ cm^3$ (3 cm × 3 cm × 3 cm)

$M = 243\ g$

(c) $D = M/V$

So, $V \times D = M$

So, $V = M/D$

So, $V = \dfrac{840\,g}{1.2\,g/cm^3}$

$V = 700\ cm^3$

Exercise 12.3: Solids, liquids and gases

1. Copy out and complete this table about the properties of solids, liquids and gases

	Solids	Liquids	Gases
Do they flow easily?	No	Yes	Yes
Can they be compressed?	No	No	Yes
Can they change their shape?	Not easily	Yes	Yes
Are the particles close together or far apart?	Close together	Close together	Far apart
Do the particles hold onto each other tightly or not?	Yes	No	No

2. (a) Solid

(b) Gas

(c) Liquid

(d) Gas

(e) Solid

(f) Liquid

3. (a) The particles in the air bounce around inside the tyre this causes pressure inside the tyre.

    (b) The air pressure increases when the mechanics pump up the tyre because more particles are introduced into the same space. There are more particles bouncing around, so more pressure is created.

    (c) The air pressure inside the tyre rises as it gets hotter because the particles have more energy (kinetic) and move faster. They hit each other and the walls of the tyre harden, causing an increase in pressure.

    (d) Tyres that contain air absorb some of the bumps on the racing circuit because the **particles can be pushed closer together**.

Internet project

Check pupils' investigations into barometers.

Chapter 13

Exercise 13.1: Pure substance or mixture?

1.   To check that a mixture of sand, salt and sugar actually contained several different types of particle one would **separate the components of the mixture and show that they have different properties**. Two approaches could be taken:

   –   Either add water to the mixture – stir and then filter out the sand. Then use chromatography to separate the salt and sugar (this is quite tricky as both are colourless).

   –   Or use a magnifying glass to look at a sample of the mixture. Sand is eay to distinguish, but the sugar and salt crystals may look similar.

2.   To check a delicatessen's claim one would check the boiling point of the liquid. Pure water boils at 100°C.

3.   Because more than one substance is listed and a pure substance cannot be a mixture of substances!

4.   You would use a magnet. Only the iron filings would be magnetic. If the metallic powder contained magnesium particles they would be left behind. Magnesium is not magnetic.

Exercise 13.2: Solutions and solubility

1.

Word	Definition
Dissolve	What happens when one substance seems to disappear when it is mixed with a liquid
Concentrated	A solution with many solute particles in a small volume of solvent
Dilute	A solution with very few solute particles
Solute	The name for a substance that dissolves in a liquid
Soluble	This means 'can dissolve'
Solvent	The name for the liquid part of a solution
Solution	A mixture of a solvent and a solute
Insoluble	This means 'cannot dissolve'
Saturated	A solution that cannot accept any more solute
Solubility	The amount of a substance that will dissolve in a liquid

2.   (a)   Solutes: sugar, phosphoric acid, and salt

          Solvent: water

   (b)   To make sure that the solutes dissolve quickly in the solvent they would **raise the temperature and stir when the solutes are added**.

3. (a) Input variable: Temperature of water.

    (b) Outcome variable: The amount of sugar that can be dissolved.

    (c) Fair test criteria: The same volume of water has been used and there has been the same amount of stirring.

    (d) In this instance the input variable is lump size. The outcome variable would be the time taken for the lump to dissolve. The temperature, the volume of water and the amount of stirring are the variables that must remain fixed to ensure that this is a fair test.

Extension question

4. **A graph to show the results of an investigation into the solubility of sugar in water**

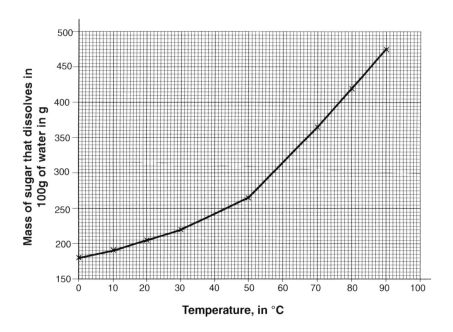

    (b) 240 – 245 g

    (c) 662.5 g

    (d) Factors that they would need to be kept constant if this was to be a fair test:
        – the size of sugar particles;
        – the amount of stirring;
        – the volume of water.

    (e) Reliability of the results could be improved by:
        – repeating the experiment and taking mean (average) of the results; and
        – use smaller increments of temperature.

Exercise 13.3: Separating mixtures

1.   (a) Most natural substances are **mixtures**, that is they are not pure. The particles of each substance in a mixture are not **identical** to each other and so these substances can often be separated because they have different **physical** properties.

     (b) There are several different ways of separating substances, including **chromatography**, which can separate different soluble substances in a mixture and **evaporation**, which can provide pure crystals of a solute from a solution.

     (c) The process of distillation depends on the fact that different substances have different **boiling points**. The process can be used to collect **gold/salt** from seawater and **alcohol** from beer or wine.

2.   (a) The different substances in the sweepings can be separated from each other by first mixing with water and stirring. Only the salt would dissolve. The mixture could then be filtered. The salt could then be collected by evaporation of the salty water. The other substances would be collected in the filter paper. They could then be separated as follows:
        – iron filings are magnetic so could be collected by a magnet;
        – sand and aluminium shavings have different appearances and might be separated by sieving (dependent on size of shavings): More astute pupils are likely to say that sand and aluminium cannot be satisfactorily separated by physical methods.

     (b) He could use anhydrous copper sulphate. If water is present it turns blue.

3.   (a) This method of separation is called **chromatography**

     (b) Green, brown, yellow and violet.

     (c) Four, E104, E110, E113, E122

     (d) Orange, brown and yellow.

Chapter 14

Exercise 14.1: Acids and bases

1. Pickling foods in vinegar provides an acid environment that prevents the multiplication of most bacteria.

2. Check pupils' answers, Examples could be nitric acid in production of fertilisers and explosives, sulphuric acid in making fertilisers, paints and plastics and in car batteries; hydrochloric acid in the processing of metals and purification of ores.

3. An alkali is a solution of a metal oxide in water. Check pupils' answers. Many alkalis are used in cleaning products (e.g. oven cleaner, toothpaste, soap).

4. Acids and alkalis are **corrosive**, which means that they can cause damage to the skin. If one of these substances is split or splashed onto the skin, plenty of cold water must be run over the splashed area. In the laboratory, you should always add **acid** to **water**, and never the other way round. When working with acids or alkalis you should always wear **overalls/lab coat** and **goggles/eye protection**.

Extension questions

5. Hydrochloric acid helps:
    – In the digestion of proteins. It provides ideal conditions for the enzyme involved in the digestion of protein.
    – It kills harmful bacteria in food.

    Hydrochloric acid can be harmful because it can damage the lining of stomach (causing ulcers) or the base of the gullet (causing heartburn).

6. Check pupils' answers. An **antioxidant 'mops up' oxidising agents**. These **oxidising agents can damage proteins and DNA** in cells. Antioxidants are abundant **in brightly-coloured foods** e.g. peppers, broccoli and tomatoes.

Exercise 14.2: Neutralisation

1. To make a nettle sting less painful you would rub on **a weak alkali (such as a solution of baking powder)**, or rub with a dock leaf.

2. This shows that the aspirin solution is a weak acid.

3. (a) D   (b) B, C, E   (c) A   (d) B

Extension questions

4. The antacids would be the input variable. The amount of antacid required to neutralise an acid would be the outcome variable. Fixed variables (to make it a fair test) would be the volume of acid used and the type of acid used. The temperature during the experiment would also remain fixed. Remember that most powerful antacid will require smallest amount to neutralise the acid.

The apparatus needed for this experiment would include:
- Pestle and mortar for grinding up the tablets.
- Weighing machine to determine fixed mass of remedy.
- 4 beakers (or conical flasks) each containing 10 cm³ of acid – each beaker labelled e.g. A, B, C, D.
- Water to dissolve remedies.
- Four 20 cm³ syringes containing the four antacids to be tested – each syringe labelled e.g. A, B, C, D.
- Test tube rack if test tubes are used instead of beakers.
- Full range or universal indicator to determine point of neutralisation.
- White tile or plain white paper to place under testing flask/beaker.
- Eye protectors.

The method would be:
- Set up equipment needed.
- Place 10 cm³ (fixed value for each) of acid in each beaker/flask.
- Add 2/3 drops of indicator and make a note of the colour.
- Grind up each antacid tablet and dissolve each in a fixed volume of water, separate beakers labelled A, B, C, D.
- Use syringe for first antacid solution and add (2 cm³ at a time) to acid in beaker, swirling after each addition until neutral green is obtained.
- Record volume of antacid used to neutralise the acid.
- Repeat the process for the remaining three antacid remedies.
- Compare the recorded volumes of each antacid used to neutralise the acid and reach a conclusion to the experiment.

5. (a) **A graph to show the results of a neutralisation reaction**

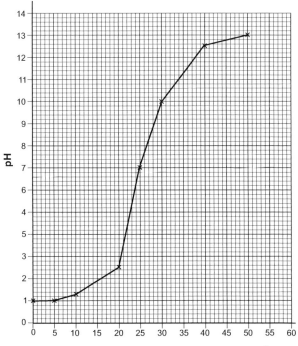

Volume of sodium hydroxide added in cm³

(b)   Check pupils' answers. Make sure they demonstrate an understanding of neutralisation and the point at which neutralisation occurs.

(c)   They could improve their results by:
– repeating the experiment several times and using mean result; and
– use smaller increments of volume of sodium hydroxide added, particularly close to the neutralisation point.

Exercise 14.3: More reactions of acids

1.   (a)   zinc + **hydrochloric acid** ⟶ zinc chloride + hydrogen

     (b)   nitric acid + magnesium ⟶ **magnesium nitrate** + **water**

     (c)   **sulphuric acid** + potassium hydroxide ⟶ potassium sulphate + **water**

     (d)   copper carbonate + hydrochloric acid ⟶ **copper chloride** + **carbon dioxide** + **water**

     (e)   lead + **sulphuric acid** ⟶ lead sulphate + **water**

2.   (a)   Copper chloride: **hydrochloric acid and copper oxide**

     (b)   Lead nitrate: **nitric acid and lead oxide**

     (c)   Iron chloride: **hydrochloric acid and iron oxide**

     (d)   Zinc sulphate: **sulphuric acid and zinc oxide**

3.   The acid could react with the metal, but would not react with glass.

4.   (a)   You tell that this is a chemical change because **a gas is released.**

     (b)   **Carbon dioxide** is the gas given off. Carbon dioxide **turns limewater milky.**

     (c)   You can tell when the reaction is finished because **no more gas is given off.**

     (d)   Calcium chloride

     (e)   Evaporate the solution very slowly.

5.   Acids react with most metals to produce a **salt** and a gas called **hydrogen**. This gas makes a (**squeaky**) **pop** when tested with a lighted splint. Acids react with a **carbonate** to make a salt, water and carbon dioxide gas. Limestone contains the compound **calcium carbonate**, which can be dissolved by acid in rainwater.

Extension questions

6. The acid in the fruit will react with iron but not with copper.

7. (a)

A graph to show the results of an experiment to investigate the reaction between marble chips and dilute hydrochloric acid

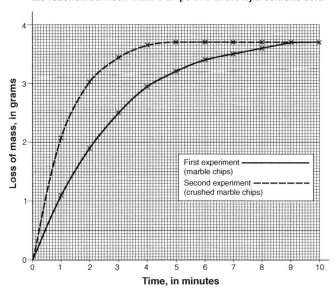

(b) The **second experiment** goes the fastest at the start of the reaction.

(c) The reaction has finished. There is a finite mass of hydrochloric acid and at this stage there are no more molecules of hydrochloric acid to react with the marble chips. No more calcium chloride can be produced, no more carbon dioxide will be released. The mass becomes constant after 9 minutes.

(d) An increased surface area increases the rate of a chemical reaction.

Project

Check pupils' project on catalytic converters. The main points of the project should include:

- Changing carbon monoxide and nitrogen oxide to carbon dioxide, water and nitrogen.

- Pupils should appreciate the large surface area that the gas passes over, and the catalyst (rhodium or platinum) that increases the rate of conversion of harmful emissions to less harmful ones. Details of how catalysts work would not be expected at this level. It is the end result that is important.

Chapter 15

Exercise 15.1: The Periodic Table

1. **Elements** are substances that cannot be broken down into simpler substances. Some, such as carbon, are made of particles called **atoms** and others, such as oxygen, are made of particles called **molecules.** There are about **a hundred** of these substances – the heaviest ones can only be made during **nuclear** reactions.

2. Carbon, magnesium, sulphur, lead

Exercise 15.2: Metals and non-metals

1. (a) Non-metals

    (b) Oxygen; neon / argon / helium

    (c) Oxygen (in water!); hydrogen

    (d) Mercury; diamond (allow carbon)

    (e) Conductors; Insulators; Particle

2. (a) **A pie chart to show the percentage, by weight, of different elements in the Earth's crust**

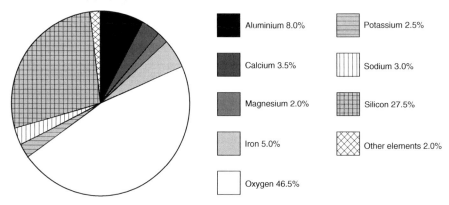

    (b) Aluminium

    (c) In sand (silicon dioxide)

    (d) Only iron is magnetic so you would use a magnet.

    (e) Carbon/hydrogen

Exercise 15.3: Compounds

1.

Name of substance	Solid, liquid or gas	Colour	Is it flammable?	Any special property
Iron	Solid	Grey-black	No	Magnetic
Sulphur	Solid	Yellow-green	No	No
Iron sulphide	Solid	Black	No	No
Oxygen	Gas	Colourless	No	Supports combustion
Hydrogen	Gas	Colourless	Yes	Burns with a pop
Water	Liquid	Colourless	No	Excellent solvent

2. A compound contains two or more elements that are chemically combined. Its chemical properties are entirely different from those of the elements from which it is made.

Al_2O_3 NaCl   HCl   Co H_2O are all compounds

3. (a) sodium, nigrogen and oxygen

(b) magnesium, carbon and oxygen

(c) calcium and carbon

(d) nitrogen, hydrogen and oxygen

(e) aluminium and oxygen

(f) hydrogen, sulphur and oxygen

4. (a) (ii) and (vi)

(b) (i), (iii) and (vii)

(c) (iv), (v) and (viii)

(d) (ii)

(e) (i), (iii), (iv), (v), (vi) and (vii)

Extension question

5. (a) C, D   (b) E   (c) B   (d) F

Chapter 16

Exercise 16.1: Chemical reactions

1. You might see **fizzing, colour change and a new product being formed** when a chemical change takes place.

2. You may hear **fizzing or popping** when a chemical change takes place.

3. (a) sodium + chlorine ➝ sodium chloride

    (b) Believe that a chemical change has taken place because **thermal energy is given off, there is a change in colour and a different solid is formed**.

4. (a) (i) magnesium + **oxygen** ➝ **magnesium oxide**
        (ii) Magnesium oxide has more mass than magnesium. The extra mass is oxygen from the air

    (b) oxygen

    (c) zinc oxide

    (d) A – chemical; B – chemical; C – physical

Exercise 16.2: Important chemical changes

1.

Time (min)	Volume of dough (cm³)
0	24 (allow 25)
5	32 (allow 33, 34)
10	42 (allow 43)
15	64 (allow 65)
20	72 (allow 73)
25	72 (allow 73)
30	72 (allow 73)

(a) **A graph to show how the amount of dough changes over the half-hour period**

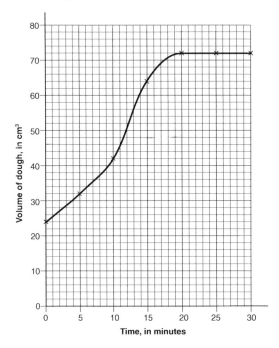

(b) 11 – 12 minutes

(c) (i) The input variable would be the **amount of sugar**

(ii) The outcome (dependent) variable in this experiment would be the **volume of dough.**

(iii) For this experiment to be a fair test the baker would need to **control the temperature (by using a water bath and a thermometer) and the initial volume of dough (by using a measuring cylinder)**.

2. Check pupils' answers. Examples could be:

Useful natural chemical reactions: fermentation, respiration, photosynthesis, digestion.

Not useful natural chemical reactions: rusting, decay, weathering of buildings.

3. Check pupils have selected ten substances that could be found in their homes. Check they have identified any chemical reactions correctly and that they have found out which reactants were needed to make it.

Exercise 16.3: Burning

1. Wood

2. Putting a blanket over burning wood **prevents supply of the oxygen needed for combustion, and so helps to extinguish the fire**.

3. (a)

Type of fuel	Units of thermal energy released	Amount of fuel burned in grams	Units of thermal energy from 100 grams of fuel
Coal	40	60	66.7
Gas	54	80	67.5
Paraffin	36	50	72
Petrol	60	50	120
Diesel oil	54	75	72

It is important to complete the final column to allow a like for like comparison (i.e. you are comparing the performance of a fixed mass of fuel).

(b) The same amount of oxygen must be available in each case other wise the experiment would not be a **fair test** and the results would therefore be unreliable.

(c) **A bar chart to show how much energy is given out when fuel burns**

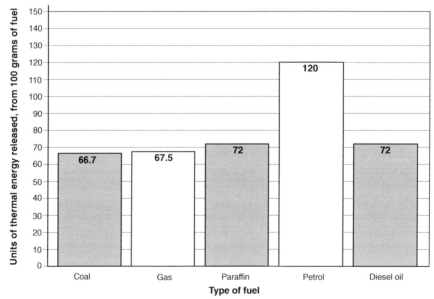

On the evidence of this experiment, petrol would seem to be the most useful heating fuel. But its expensive nature would rule it out. Diesel oil and paraffin are the next most efficient fuels, but there are problems of storage – as there are with coal. Gas would seem to be the most practical even though its efficiency is slightly less than diesel oil and paraffin.

Exercise 16.4: Air pollution

1. To test if a sample of rain was acidic you would use **an indicator.** For example **if you used universal indicator it would turn pink / orange in the presence of acid.**

2. We say that carbon dioxide is a 'greenhouse' gas because it acts like the glass in a greenhouse. It keeps the thermal energy close to the Earth's surface, and so causes warming.

Extension questions

3. (a)

Concentration of sodium disulphite (%)	Number of seeds germinated out of twenty (five experiments)					Percentage germination
0.00	19	19	17	20	18	18.6
0.05	18	19	18	19	19	18.6
0.10	12	13	14	11	12	12.4
0.50	0	1	0	0	1	0.4
2.50	0	0	0	0	0	0.0

(b)

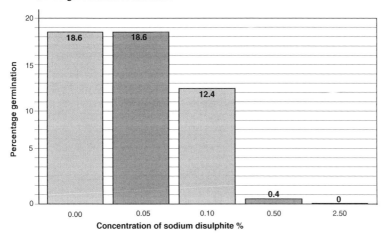

A bar chart to show the effects of sodium dioxide on the germination of oat seeds

(c) The experiment was repeated five times to enable the students to find the mean result. This gives a more accurate result.

(d) A control is used to show the germination rate when water is available but no sulphur dioxide.

(e) 0.10%

(f) They could reduce the increments of sodium disulphite between 0.05 and 0.10% to get a more accurate value.

(g) Input variable – concentration of sodium disulphite

Outcome – percentage germination

Controlled variables might be temperature, availability of water, and the availability of oxygen

(h) (i) Burning fossil fuels e.g. in thermal power stations, releases large amounts of sulphur dioxide into the natural environment. Industry produces most of the SO_2. Cars etc. produce carbon and nitrogen oxides because most petrol is low sulphur these days.

    (ii) Other effects could be:
- irritation of lungs
- reduced photosynthesis
- acidification of lakes preventing growth of crustaceans

4. (a)

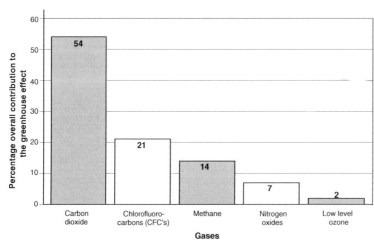

A bar chart to show the sources and effects of greenhouse gases

(b) Effect of water 2%

(c) Carbon dioxide and methane

(d) A green house gas acts like the glass in a greenhouse. It keeps thermal energy close to the Earth's surface, and so causing warming.

(e) Harmful effects of greenhouse gases:
- melting of ice caps
- flooding
- spread of pests
- altered weather patterns, including storms

(f) (i) Less carbon dioxide from burning and less methane from cattle. Forests are big users of CO_2 during photosynthesis.

    (ii) Less burning of fossil fuels to provide thermal energy for houses.

    (iii) Less burning of fossil fuels to provide electricity.

(g) (i) 0.005%

    (ii) 0.020%

    (iii) A vast increase in the number of cars in the world has led to a much greater use of fossil fuels.

Exercise 16.5: Conservation of mass

1.   From the results of this experiment we can make several observations. Firstly note that the mass of the crucible remains the same, 50 g. This allows us to calculate what happens to the mass of the contents before and after heating. The mass of the magnesium ribbon before heating is 12 g. After heating the contents of the crucible (now magnesium oxide) have increased in mass to 20 g. The additional mass of 8 g is the result of the combination of oxygen from the air with the magnesium ribbon to form magnesium oxide.

Chapter 17

Exercise 17.1: The reactivity series

1. (a) Zinc is more reactive.

    (b) zinc + silver nitrate ⟶ **zinc nitrate + silver**

2. (a) Copper heated with iron oxide: Very slow reaction (iron close to copper in reactivity series) but iron oxide and copper will be formed.

    (b) Magnesium placed in dilute hydrochloric acid: The reaction occurs quickly (hydrogen is given off and can be tested with a lighted splint – a (squeaky) pop should be heard).

    (c) Copper placed in dilute sulphuric acid: No reaction takes place, because copper is lower than hydrogen in the reactivity series.

    (d) Magnesium placed in copper nitrate solution: The magnesium displaces the copper from the copper nitrate to form magnesium nitrate and copper.

    (e) Silver warmed with water: At this level it is fair to say that no reaction takes place as silver is lower than hydrogen in the reactivity series.

Extension question

3. (a) You could test to see what metal M is by carrying out a series of experiments, where the Metal M is added to the different solutions of metal salts. You would look for any displacement reactions that may take place (see table on p233 *Science Book 2*) between the unknown metal and the solutions provided. Metals displace one another in regular order so we can use the evidence of the reactions we collect to place the unknown metal in the Reactivity Series.

    (b) The gas given off is hydrogen and can be tested with a lighted splint – a (squeaky) pop should be heard.

    (c) The gas is carbon dioxide. Its identity could be tested by bubbling it through lime water. If it is carbon dioxide the lime water will turn milky.

Exercise 17.2: Corrosion

1. (a) Corrosion involves a reaction between a **metal** and some substance in the **environment/atmosphere**. In most cases an **oxide** is formed on the surface of the metal.

    (b) Rusting is the corrosion of **iron** and **steel**. This is a dangerous process because the **rust/hydrated iron oxide** is weak and brittle. Rusting can be prevented by coating the metal with, for example, **plastic/paint/zinc**. Another method of prevention involves 'sacrificing' a second metal, such as **zinc/magnesium**.

2. (a) iron + water + oxygen ⟶ hydrated iron oxide

    (b) Cars rust more quickly in England than in California because there is **more water in the atmosphere** in England.

    (c) By **painting or galvanising**.

3. (a) Galvanising is such an effective method of protection because it offers **two levels of protection: barrier and sacrificial.**

    (b) Examples could be: buckets, baths, fence posts, cars and bridge supports.

    (c) Coating cannot be used for preventing corrosion of railway lines because it would be worn away by the abrasion of locomotive wheels.

4. (a) **A chart to show the results of a rusting experiment**

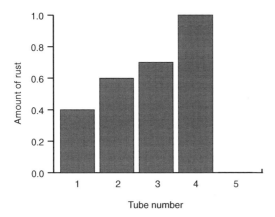

    (b) Warmth / temperature had the bigger effect on rusting. This can be deduced by comparing tubes 3 and 4 with tubes 1 and 2.

    (c) The fifth tube: 0 Assume that the boiled water will have no oxygen, and no oxygen can enter from the air because of the oil layer. No rusting is possible without air.

Extension questions

5. Design of a fair test to investigate whether galvanising offers double protection for steel.

    Input variable will be level of protection

    Outcome variable will be extent of rusting

    Method: Compare the extent of rusting seen on a galvanised nail with a scratched galvanised nail and a bare steel nail.

    Controlled variables might include temperature, access to oxygen, water and time before the results are collected.

6. Check pupils' investigations into stainless steel. Check for mentions of how it is different from iron: stainless steel contains iron, nickel and chromium. The alloy of these metals does not rust because a surface layer of chromium oxide forms and prevents damp air getting to the iron. The layer is very strong, despite being very thin – less than 0.000 000 01 m thick.

    There are two process routes for making steel, the electric arc furnace and the basic oxygen converter. The latter requires molten iron, which is produced in blast furnaces. The raw materials for producing molten iron are iron ore, coking coal and fluxes (materials that help the chemical process) – mainly limestone.

    The coals and ores are carefully blended. Blended coal is first heated in coke ovens to produce coke.

    Fine-sized ore is first mixed with coke and fluxes and heated in a sinter plant. This is a continuous moving belt on which the coke is ignited. The high temperatures generated fuse the ore particles and fluxes together to form a porous clinker called sinter. The use of sinter in the blast furnace helps make the ironmaking process more efficient.

Iron ore lumps and pellets, coke, sinter and possibly extra flux are carried to the top of the blast furnace on a conveyor or in skips and then tipped, or charged, into the furnace. Hot air (900 °C etc.) is blased into the bottom of the furnace through nozzles. The oxygen in the air combusts with the coke to form carbon monoxide gas, and this generates a great deal of thermal energy.

The carbon monoxide flows up through the blast furnace and removes oxygen from the iron ores on their way down, thereby leaving iron. The thermal energy in the furnace melts the iron, and the resulting liquid iron (or hot metal as it is called in the industry) is tapped at regular intervals by opening a hole in the bottom of the furnace and allowing it to flow out.

The hot metal flows into torpedo ladles. These are specially constructed railway containers which transport iron, still in liquid form, to the steel furnace.

The iron produced by the blast furnace has a carbon conent of 4 to 4.5% as well as a number of other "impurities". This makes it relatively brittle. Steelmaking refines the iron, amongst other things by reducing its carbon content, to make it a stronger and more manipulable product.

The BOS (Basic Oxygen Steelmaking) process is the major modern process for making bulk steels. Scrap steel is first charged into the vessel, followed by hot metal (liquid iron) from the blast furnace. A water-cooled lance is lowered into the vessel through which very pure oxygen is blown at high pressure. The oxygen, through a process known as oxidation, combines with the carbon, and with other unwanted elements, separating them from the metal, leaving steel.

The steel is tapped into a ladle, in which secondary steelmaking frequently takes place.

The electric arc furnace (EAF) (together with the basic oxygen vessel) is another one of the two modern ways of making steel. Unlike the basic oxygen route, the EAF does not use hot metal. It is charged with "cold" material. This is normally steel scrap (recycled goods made from steel which have reached the end of their useful life). Steel scrap (or other ferrous material) is first tipped into the EAF from an overhead crane. A lid is then swung into position over the furnace. This lid contains electrodes which are lowered into the furnace. An electric current is passed through the electrodes to form an arc. The thermal energy generated by this arc melts the scrap.

During the melting process, other metals (ferro-alloys) are added to the steel to give it the required chemical composition.

(Note: This is more detailed than needed at this level, but hopefully useful for those teachers who are not familiar with the iron and steel industry.)

7. (a)

Mass of magnesium in g	Starting temperature in °C	Final temperature in °C	Rise in temperature in °C
0.00	22	22	0
0.25	23	30	7
0.50	23	38	15
0.75	22	46	24
1.00	22	55	33
1.25	22	61	39
1.50	23	68	45
1.75	24	69	45
2.00	23	68	45
2.25	22	67	45
2.50	23	68	45

(b) copper sulphate + magnesium ➙ copper + magnesium sulphate

(c) The input (independent) variable for this reaction is the mass of magnesium.

(d) The outcome (dependent) variable in this experiment is the rise in temperature.

(e) Exothermic

(f) **A graph to show the results of an investigation into how much change in thermal energy went on when magnesium reacted with copper sulphate solution.**

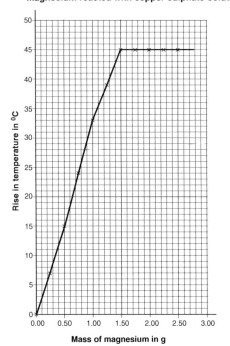

(g) The curve increases (i.e. the temperature rises) as the amount of magnesium is increased. At 1.50 grams the curve plateaus because at this stage all the copper sulphate has reacted and the reaction ceases and so no more rises in thermal energy are recorded.

(h) Fair test criteria: Fixed amount of copper sulphate; a fixed starting temperature and a fixed volume of vessel.

(i) Total mass at the end of the experiment is **26.5g.** This is because during this chemical change there is **conservation of mass**. This means the total mass of the reactants used is the same as the total mass of the products formed.

Exercise 17.3: Extraction of metals

1. Some metals, such as **gold** and silver, are found as the uncombined metal in nature. Most metals are found combined as **compounds/oxides** in **ores**, such as haematite and bauxite. There are three stages in the extraction of a metal: **mining**, **decomposition** (which always involves some chemical reactions) and **purification** (which makes the metal suitable for use).

2.

Metal	Main ore	One important use of the metal	Method of extraction
gold	found native	jewellery/electrical contacts	mining
iron	haematite	building materials/any suitable example	heating with carbon
copper	malachite	wire for the conduction of electricity	direct heating/heating with carbon
aluminium	bauxite	cooking utensils/cars/aircraft	electrolysis
mercury	cinnabar	thermometers	heating in air

3. (a) mercury oxide ➝ mercury + oxygen

    (b) tin oxide + carbon ➝ tin + carbon dioxide

    (c) calcium oxide ➝ calcium + oxygen

Chapter 18

Exercise 18.1: Energy

1. (a) To carry out any action, **energy** is needed. All of these different types of action can be called **work**. Energy comes in different forms. For example **potential** energy is stored in materials that have been stretched or bent. **Kinetic** energy is the energy of movement. **Thermal** energy is the result of fast-moving particles in hot objects.

   (b) Energy cannot be created or destroyed, but it can be **transformed/transferred** from one form to another. For example, a torch changes **electrical** energy into **light** energy. Energy is measured in units called **joules**.

2. 20 000 joules

3.

Machine (transducer)	Energy is changed from	to (mainly)
Radio	Electrical	Sound
Toaster	Electrical	Thermal
Fan	Electrical	Kinetic
Motor car	Chemical	Kinetic
Catapult	Potential	Kinetic
Torch	Electrical	Light

4. (a) Throwing a ball up into the air: **kinetic – potential – kinetic – (thermal)**

   (b) Pulling on the brakes of your mountain bike   **kinetic – thermal**

5. When an action is completed (work is done) the total amount of energy at the end will be the same as the total amount of energy at the start. The energy at the start will change into other forms as the work is done. In most cases, energy will be radiated away in the form of thermal energy, which is why perpetual motion is not possible as this energy 'lost/wasted' as thermal energy has to be replaced by a further input of energy to keep the body/motor moving. So the statement is true.

Exercise 18.2: Energy resources

1. (a) A fuel is a store of **energy** which can be released by burning in air. The air supplies the gas **oxygen** required for the burning process. Burning a candle shows that **thermal** energy and kinetic (light) energy are given out during the burning process. In the laboratory a **Bunsen** burner can give a controllable supply of thermal energy by the burning of **natural gas**.

   (b) Coal and gas are examples of **fossil** fuels – once they are burned they cannot be replaced. Water and wind power are **renewable** energy resources because they can be naturally replaced and so will not run out.

Extension questions

2. (a)

Use of energy	Percentage of total energy used
Industry	29
Domestic (in homes)	31
Transport	26
Other uses	14

(b)

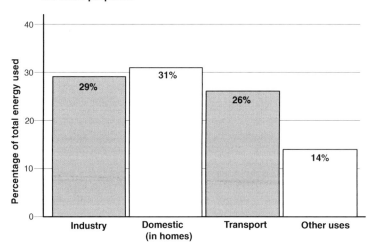

A chart to show how energy is used for other purposes

(c) Any suitable examples e.g. horticultural and farming, recreation (sports grounds/funfairs), theatres, hospitals, schools, shopping centres.

(d) Any suitable examples e.g. radio, microwave, oven, kettle, dishwasher, or lighting, central heating, vacuum cleaner.

3. (a)

Source	Percentage of total energy
Oil	1.5
Natural gas	38.5
Coal	30.0
Nuclear	26.3
Water	1.5
Others	**2.2**

(b) Wind

(c) **A pie chart to show the sources of energy generated in the United Kingdom**

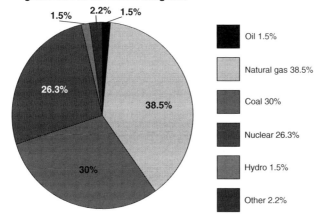

■ Oil 1.5%

□ Natural gas 38.5%

■ Coal 30%

■ Nuclear 26.3%

■ Hydro 1.5%

■ Other 2.2%

(d) Coal and oil are non-renewable and cause air pollution and contribute towards global warming by emission of greenhouse gasses.

(e) We should use more nuclear power, because it does not produce air pollution and the lifetime is much, much longer than fossil fuels.

We are anxious about using nuclear power, because the radioactive waste needs to be stored very safely.

Exercise 18.3: Fossil fuels

1. ● 300 million years ago there were huge forests of simple, fern-like trees.
   ● The Sun shone onto the Earth, and trees absorbed light energy from the Sun.
   ● When trees died, they fell into swamps but did not decompose.
   ● More trees fell on top.
   ● The rivers washed sediment on top.
   ● The material was heated under pressure for millions of years.
   ● Coal is a store of chemical energy.

2. ● The Sun shone on the Earth and tiny plants in the sea obtained their energy from the Sun.
   ● The plants were eaten by small animals in the sea.
   ● The small organisms died.
   ● When the seas dried up, the small organisms became trapped.
   ● Movements of the Earth compressed the remains of the small organisms.
   ● Conditions change, so that some bodies are allowed to decay.
   ● Over millions of years, gas given off from the decay processes is trapped.
   ● Thermal energy and pressure changed the material in the bodies of plants and animals into oil.
   ● People build oil platforms to drill for oil.
   ● Gas is collected from above the oil wells.
   ● Gas pipelines bring gas to homes and factories

3.   It is important to conserve fuels because there are **limited supplies** and **combustion causes pollution** and releases greenhouse gases which contribute to global warming.

4.   Wood is popular in Norway because it is **freely available.**

Extension question

5.   (a)   **A graph to show the use of coal, oil and natural gas in the European Community (1973 - 1989)**

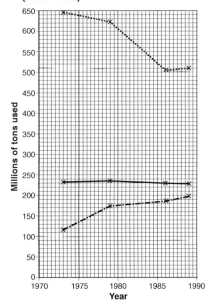

(b)   Natural gas in 1973 accounted for 12% of total fossil fuels.

(c)   Since 1970 there has not been an increase in the total use of fossil fuels but there has been a shift out of oil into using more natural gas.

Exercise 18.4: Renewable energy resources

1.

Renewable energy resource	How this resource is valuable
Solar energy	Can heat water or generate electricity
Geothermal energy	Thermal energy from underground rocks
Wind	Can move small boats or turn wind turbines
Tides and waves	Seawater turns a turbine
Hydroelectric power	Water current turns a turbine
Biomass	Material from the growth of plants

2.   We describe electricity as the most useful form of energy because it **can easily be changed into other forms of energy**.

3.   (a)   **A pie chart to show the contribution of each energy resource to all renewable energy resources.**

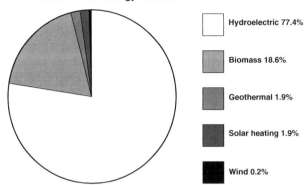

Hydroelectric 77.4%

Biomass 18.6%

Geothermal 1.9%

Solar heating 1.9%

Wind 0.2%

(b)   **Biomass** is the most useful renewable resource in very forested parts of the world.

(c)   Geothermal energy makes such a small contribution because **there are few places where the Earth's underground thermal energy is accessible on the Earth's surface.**

4.   (a)   The black cloth balloon.

(b)   Black

(c)   It is important to use the same volume of water in each balloon **so that there is only one variable – a fair test.**

(d)   You would use one type of material that is available in shiny and dull versions e.g. metal foil.

5.   **Renewable** means that the fuel can be replaced naturally. **Reusable** means that it can be used more than once. (Note: reusable is a term that is never used when talking about energy because once energy has been used, i.e. changed into another form, it cannot be used again.)

Exercise 18.5: Energy conservation

1.   Reserves of **fossil** fuels will eventually run out, so energy **conservation** is necessary. We can use more **renewable** energy sources which will also reduce **pollution**. Humans can use less energy by **cycling** or **walking** instead of driving everywhere. We can also save energy by cutting down thermal energy losses from our buildings. **Insulation** can reduce loss of thermal energy from walls and roofs, while double-glazing can reduce loss of thermal energy through **windows** and **doors**.

2. The answer to this question will depend on the degree of energy conservation found in the pupils' homes.

Do you have	Yes or no
Cavity wall insulation	
Roof insulation	
Double glazing	
Lagging on your hot water tank	
Draught excluders on external doors	
Low energy light lamps	

Extension question

3. (a)

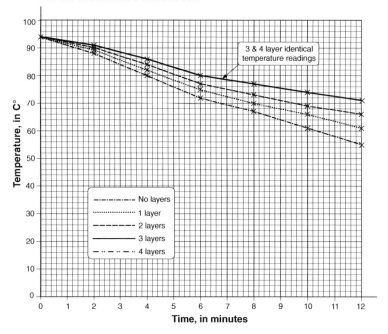

A line graph to show the results of investigation into the effectiveness of insulation

(b) The input (independent) variable in this experiment is the **number of layers of insulating material.**

(c) The outcome (dependent) variable in this experiment is the **temperature**.

(d) To make sure that this is a fair test Ted and Laura have to keep all other variable constant e.g. same material, same thickness of layers

(e) No it would not make good sense to add five layers of insulating material. This is because there is no difference in the effectiveness of insulation between three and four layers, so fifth layer would almost certainly have no effect and would be therefore be uneconomic.

Chapter 19

Exercise 19.1: Generating electricity from a fuel

1. **A turbine** is a set of blades that can turn a shaft. The turning shaft is part of a **generator**, which is a device that changes kinetic energy into electrical energy.

2. A power station needs cooling towers because a great deal of thermal energy is produced during the generation of electricity. This thermal energy must be released.

3. (a) **A bar chart to show the percentage efficiency of different power stations.**

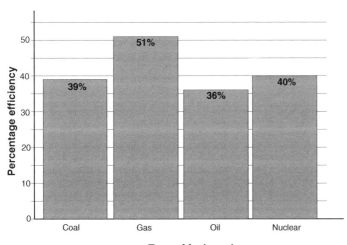

   (b) We would like to use less coal in power stations because coal burning causes smoke and acid rain and because coal reserves are being used up.

   (c) Some people object to the use of nuclear power stations because they worry about release of radioactive wastes.

Exercise 19.2: Electricity and energy

1. Answers for working safely with electricity could include:
   – Keep water away
   – Don't stick anything into a power outlet
   – Ensure cables are insulated

2. A cell (battery) is a (metal) case containing chemicals which are connected to positive and negative terminals located outside. It supplies the energy needed to push an electrical current around a circuit.

3. The case of a plug is made from **plastic** because it is a good **insulator**. The pins of the plug need to **conduct** electricity, so they are made of **brass**. The covering on a wire is made of **plastic**, so that it will not conduct **electricity**. Some electrical machines use **graphite** (a kind of carbon) to conduct electricity between different parts of the motor.

Extension questions

4.   Check the pupils' choice of ten electrical appliances and that they have completed the table (see below) correctly.

Appliance	Is it powered by mains or battery?	It converts electrical energy to	Some electrical energy is wasted as

5.   The apparatus could be used to test whether a material was an insulator or a conductor as follows:

Firstly you would make sure the switch is open (turned off). You would then attach the material to be tested between to the two clips. The switch would then be turned on. If the lamp **lights up** it means the material has allowed the electricity to pass through and so is a **conductor**. If the lamp does **not light** then the material is an **insulator**.

Chapter 20

Exercise 20.1: Circuits

1. A complete circuit would require a:
   - source of electrical energy;
   - leads and wires;
   - an appliance/component.

2. Chemical potential energy

3. (a) The electrons carrying electric charge. The movement of these is called a current.

   (b) The cell/battery

   (c) The appliance/component

Exercise 20.2: Series and parallel circuits

1. A – 4; B – 5; C – 1; D – 2; E – 3

2. Electricity can pass through any material that is a **conductor**. A complete circuit lets **current** flow all the way round it. The energy can be supplied by a cell and can pass from one component to another through a lead. When a circuit is made up it may include a **switch**, which can be opened to stop the flow of current. If the **switch** is closed then a component such as a **lamp** will light or a **buzzer** will sound.

3.

Feature	Series circuit	Parallel circuit
Current in different places	The same	Not the same
Number of pathways that current can take	One	Several
Effect of one damaged component	All components stop working	Other parallel circuits still work
Effect of opening a switch	All components stop working	Other parallel circuits still work

4. (a) Lamps 1 and 2 will light up, and lamp 3 will not light.

   (b) 1.0 A

   (c) 1.6 A

5. (a) The lamps would be brighter in the **parallel** circuit.

   (b) The **parallel** circuit would have the highest voltage across each lamp.

   (c) The **series** circuit would be the cheapest to use.

Extension questions

6. Check pupils' circuit diagrams and use of symbols of the model they have chosen.

7. (a)

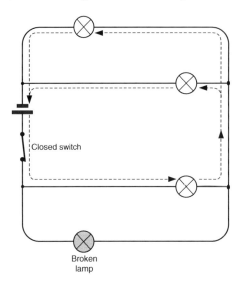

Closed switch

Broken
lamp

(b) Because this is a parallel circuit when one lamp blows the other lamps stay on (flow marked by the dotted line).

8.

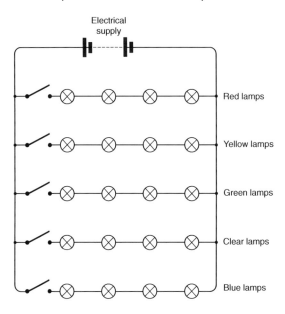

Electrical
supply

Red lamps

Yellow lamps

Green lamps

Clear lamps

Blue lamps

Exercise 20.3: Problems with circuits

1. (A) The lamp

(B) Extension lead with switch.

Extension questions

2. Check that all possible faults are included and that the pupils have used the correct symbols. Circuit diagram of a faulty torch:

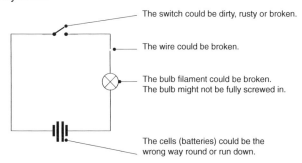

The switch could be dirty, rusty or broken.

The wire could be broken.

The bulb filament could be broken.
The bulb might not be fully screwed in.

The cells (batteries) could be the wrong way round or run down.

3. (a) Check pupils circuit for completeness and for the positioning of the ammeter.

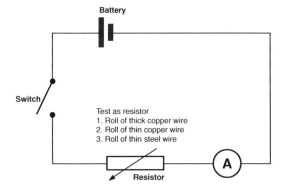

Battery

Switch

Test as resistor
1. Roll of thick copper wire
2. Roll of thin copper wire
3. Roll of thin steel wire

Resistor

A

(b) To conduct a fair test experiment to see whether thickness or length of wire is more important in affecting resistance you would:

Experiment 1:   Input variable – vary thickness of wire.

Output variable – measured flow of electrical current.

Fixed variables – same length of wire, same battery, same type of wire.

Record the electrical current through the wires of different thicknesses.

Experiment 2:   Input variable – vary lengths of wire.

Output variable – measured flow of electrical current.

Fixed variables – same thickness of wire, same battery, same type of wire.

Record the electrical current through the wires of different lengths.

The results of the experiments would then be compared to determine whether length or thickness had the greatest effect on resistance.

Chapter 21

Exercise 21.1: More electrical components

1. A fuse offers protection because it is the weakest part of a circuit and will break the circuit if too great a current flows.

2. It is dangerous because the foil will conduct current but will not break if there is a problem with the current.

Project

Pupils are required to find out the current values for different household fuses. They should have made a table to show some examples of household appliances, which should be protected by each type of fuse.

Chapter 22

Exercise 22.1: Magnets

1. (a) A magnet can be hung up so that it can move easily. If this happens, one end will point **North** and the other end will point South. The two different ends of a magnet are called the **poles**. Magnets exert forces on materials that contain **iron**.

    (b) Like poles of magnets **repel** one another, but unlike poles **attract**.

2. Check pupils' diagrams. Make sure they know that the compass needle is itself a magnet and that because it is, the N-seeking pole will point to the North. The Earth is also a magnet. Because the compass needle is magnetic, any magnetic material near it will affect the direction that the needle points.

3.

Pole of first magnet	Pole of second magnet	Do they attract or repel?	Is this a push or a pull?
N	S	Attract	Pull
N	N	Repel	Push
S	S	Repel	Push

4. When an unmagnetised nail is put into a magnetic field, it becomes **magnetised.** The South-seeking pole of a magnetised nail will be attracted to the **North** pole of a magnet, but will be **repelled** by the South-seeking pole of a magnet.

Exercise 22.2: Electromagnetism

1. (a) Reduced
    (b) Increased
    (c) Reduced
    (d) Reduced

2. The relay only uses a small current to turn on a motor.

Extension question

3. (a)

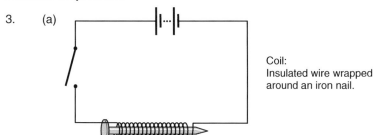

Coil:
Insulated wire wrapped around an iron nail.

Make a coil design. Ten turns of insulated wire wrapped around an iron nail. Connect the circuit as shown above, switch on and see how many paper clips can be lifted.

Repeat the experiment using 15, 20, 25, 30 turns of the insulated wire and record each time how many paper clips can be lifted. Make a table of your results.

(b) (i) Use the same thickness of insulated wire each time.

     (ii) If possible, use fresh cells each time (this experiment causes cells to run down quickly – so results of later experiments may not be reliable).

     (iii) Paper clips should be of the same size.

(c) Increasing the number of turns should increase the number of paper clips picked up.

Chapter 23

Exercise 23.1: Temperature

1. The coloured liquid in a thermometer expands on heating and moves up the tube. The tube is marked with a linear scale and the height reached by the liquid can be measured. This provides the temperature measurement.

2. Melting point of pure water: 0 °C

   Boiling point of pure water: 100 °C

3. Ice cream is not hot because the energy is locked into bonds of sugar and fat. (At this level allow: ice cream is made and stored in a fridge.)

4. 37 °C

5. The sparkler is hotter but the swimming pool has the most thermal energy because it has greater mass than the sparkler.

Extension questions

6. (a) The **degree to which the liquid inside the thermometer expands** when heated.

   (b) Alcohol is most common in school laboratory thermometers because of safety issues – mercury is poisonous and because mercury is more expensive.

   (c) A mercury thermometer

   (d) An alcohol thermometer

Exercise 23.2: Conduction and convection

1. The knife and fork are metal and conduct thermal energy away from the hand. Metal is a better conductor than wood.

2. The window feels cooler than the wooden window frame around it because glass is a better conductor than wood.

3. There are several possibilities e.g. steel, glass, cloth, wood, plastic, air

4. (a) Saucepans: The metal base conducts thermal energy for cooking and the plastic handle does not conduct thermal energy so it is safe to hold.

   (b) Sleeping bags: Air and feathers are excellent insulators so internal/thermal energy remains in body/inside sleeping bag.

5. (a) B

   (b) B

Exercise 23.3: Radiation

1. The dark green/blue one will get hotter inside. This is because the darker colour is a better absorber of radiation.

2. (a) Conduction

   (b) Dark colours absorb and re-emit thermal energy better than light colours.

   (c) Moving air carries thermal energy to the top part of the oven.

   (d) Air between the panes of glass acts as an efficient insulator.

Extension question

3. (a)

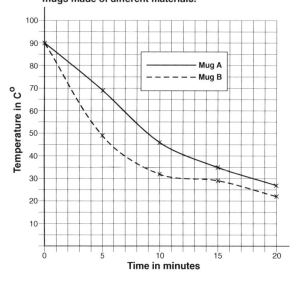

A line graph to show the results of an investigation into how quickly tea cooled in mugs made of different materials.

   (b) 73/74 °C

   (c) 12-14 minutes

   (d) 6 °C

   (e) A

   (f) Mug A was yellow and Mug B was blue because blue is a better emitter of thermal energy.

Chapter 24

Exercise 24.1: Conservation of energy

1.   TV set: Thermal energy / light / sound

2.   The thermal energy released from the lamp may set fire to the paper.

3.   (a) – (c) Thermal energy

       (d)   Thermal energy / sound

       (e)   Thermal energy

       (f) $\frac{54}{66} \times 100 = 82\%$

       (g) $\frac{6}{66} \times 100 = 9\%$

       (h) $200 - 66 = 134$ J

       (i) $\frac{6}{200} \times 100 = 3\%$

Exercise 24.2: Food and energy

1.   Check pupils have filled in the table correctly.

Food type	Energy in kJ
Flour	1495
Cereal	1485
Baked beans	306
Pasta	1559
Rice	1470

       (a)   Per 100g

       (b)   **A chart to show the energy value of different foods**

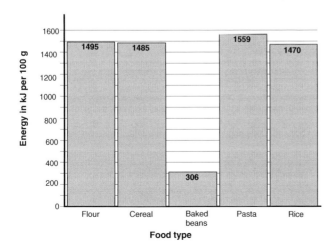

(c)   From the data, pasta would be the best as it contains the most energy per 100 g serving.

(d)   Check pupils' answers. The answer depends on the type and size of the chocolate bar chosen.

2.   (a)   Total energy used: 100 kg × 10 J × 12 m = 12 000 J
                                                                = 12 kJ

(b)   Total energy used: 50 kg × 10 J × 12 m = 6 000 J
                                                            = 6 kJ

(c)   Gena uses less energy to climb 12 m, so less work needs be done by the heart. Freddie has twice as much energy to release putting more strain on his heart than Gena.

Extension question

3.   (a)   Input (independent) variable: Type of food

(b)   Outcome (dependent) variable in this experiment: Measured change in temperature/energy released.

(c)   Constant factors: Volume of water and mass of food.

(d)   20 x 60 x 4.2 = 5040 J = 5.04 kJ

Chapter 25

Exercise 25.1: The Sun and the Earth

1.

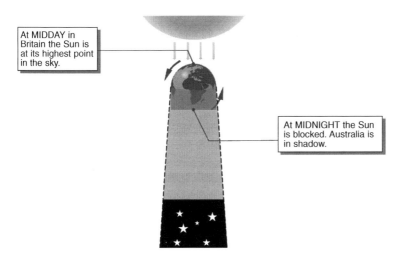

At MIDDAY in Britain the Sun is at its highest point in the sky.

At MIDNIGHT the Sun is blocked. Australia is in shadow.

2. The Earth is a **planet** that moves around the **Sun**. The Sun is at the centre of the **solar system** and is a very hot ball of glowing gas called a **star**. The **Moon** travels around the Earth and we can see it because of light **reflected** from the Sun.

3. The Sun is spherical/circular. We know this because it has the same profile from wherever it is seen.

Extension question

4. It is very unlikely that we will find organisms similar to those on Earth on any other planet because of water availability, different gravities and different atmospheres.

Exercise 25.2: Gravity and orbits

1. Planets stay in orbit because they are **moving** and because of the force of **gravity**. The force of gravity between two objects is exactly the **same** on both objects, but the **smaller** object orbits the **larger** one. A satellite has **less** mass than a planet, so the satellite is in **orbit** around the planet.

2. 1986 + 76 = 2062

3. A Plutonian 'year' is much longer than a year on Earth because its orbit is greater and so takes longer to complete.

Extension question

4.

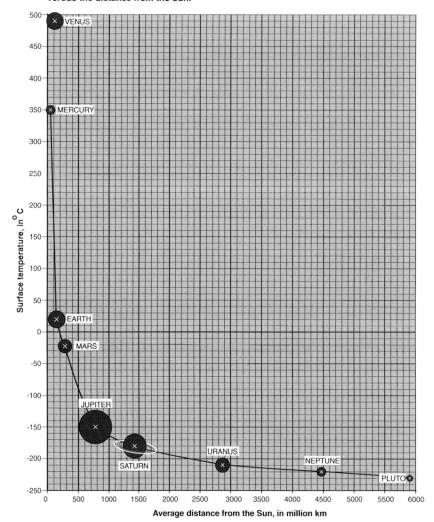

A graph to show the surface temperature of the planets versus the distance from the Sun.

(a) In general, surface temperature of a planet falls the further the planet is from the Sun. Venus is the exception.

(b) Approx 100 million km

(c) Surface temperature range: −190 to −200 °C

Exercise 25.3: Satellites

1. Geostationary

2. Low Earth orbits: military uses to follow troop movements, wildlife conservation to follow herds of animals.

3. They can receive solar radiation and need not carry heavy loads of fuel.

Extension question

4. Check pupils' investigations into how satellites directly affect our lives.

Exercise 25.4: Sun, Earth and Moon

1. (a) The Earth to orbit the Sun   1 year ($365\frac{1}{4}$ days)

   (b) The Moon to orbit the Earth   28 days

   (c) The Earth to turn once on its axis?   24 hours

2. It is colder in winter than in summer because we are further from the Sun and the days are shorter.

3. (a)

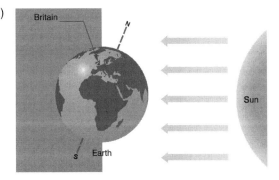

   (b) It is summer in Britain, because the North Pole is tilted towards the Sun. The Northern hemisphere receives more sunlight than the Southern Hemisphere, which makes the days longer and the land warmer, thereby giving the Northern Hemisphere its summer season.

   (c) Nighttime in Britain.

4. A shadow is formed.

5.

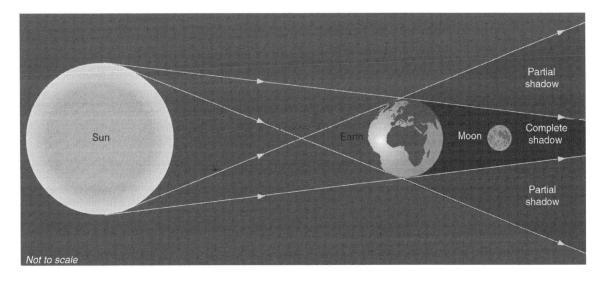

Extension questions

6. The Earth's tilt makes the North Pole face towards the Sun in summer, keeping it in sunlight 24 hours per day, even as the Earth spins. This is known as the Midnight Sun.

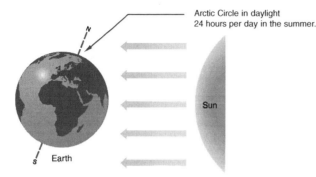

Arctic Circle in daylight
24 hours per day in the summer.

Sun

Earth

7. 13 times. The Moon orbits the Earth every 28 days and Earth orbits the Sun every 365 days, i.e. (365 / 28 = 13)

Exercise 25.5: Sun and the stars

1. (a) We can see stars because they are **luminous**. The Moon and some planets are visible because of the **reflection** of light from the **Sun**. Many stars seem to be arranged in patterns called **constellations**, and there may be several of these in a single **galaxy**.

   (b) Distances in space are so great that we need to measure them in **light-years**. All of the planets, stars, gases and dust together make up the **universe**.

2. Large telescopes for observing stars are usually built on hills well away from large cities because the air is clearer and there is less light pollution.

3. $T = \dfrac{D}{S}$

   $= \dfrac{149\,000\,000}{300\,000}$

   $= 4975$ or 8.3 mins (approx 500 sec – just over eight minutes)

Extension question

4. In 2006 the International Astronomical Union redefined a planet as a body that

   ● is in orbit around the Sun

   ● has sufficient mass so that it assumes a nearly round shape, and

   ● does not share its orbital region with other bodies of significant size

   A non-satellite body fulfilling only the first two of these criteria is classified as a 'dwarf planet', whilst a non-satellite body fulfilling only the first criterion is termed a 'small solar system body'. The redefinition remains controversial.

   According to the definition there are currently eight planets and three dwarf planets known in the solar system.

Chapter 26

Exercise 26.1: Forces

1. **Forces** are pushes or pulls, exerted by one thing on another. Forces can change the **shape** of things, change the **speed** and the **direction** of things. They have two important features: **size (magnitude)** and **direction**. These two features of a force can be shown by drawing an arrow.

2. (a) – (b) Forces can change:
    - shape (squeeze a rubber ball);
    - the speed (kick a foorball); and
    - the direction (return a tennis ball).

3.

Event	Distance in m	Time taken in seconds	Speed in m/s
Freestyle	50	28	1.8
Backstroke	100	60	1.7
Butterfly	100	56	1.8
Breaststroke	200	140	1.4
Individual medley	400	275	1.5

4.

Car number	Run 1 in seconds	Run 2 in seconds	Run 3 in seconds	Average time in seconds
1	2.40	2.50	2.60	2.50
2	2.90	2.75	2.78	2.81
3	2.35	2.55	4.90	2.45

(a) Run 3 for car 3

(b) Average speeds of the three cars: Car 1 – 2.50; Car 2 – 2.81; Car 3 – 2.45

(c) Input variable: Type of car

(d) Outcome variable: Time taken for run

(e) Fair test criteria: Keep all other variables constant e.g. track of same material, same slope and keep the gates the same distance apart.

Extension question

5. (a) Peregrine falcon

(b) Cheetah

(c) 766 miles per hour (this may change over time)

(d) 317.6 mph (this may change over time)

(e) A cheetah moves at around 100 kph = 27.8 m/s. So about 2.7 times faster.

Exercise 26.2: Distance and time

1. (a) $D = S \times T$

    $= 30 \text{ km/h} \times 1.5 \text{ hr}$

    $= 45 \text{ km}$

    (b) $D = 5 \text{ m/s} \times 20 \text{ s}$

    $= 100 \text{ m}$

    (c) $D = 50 \text{ m/s} \times 50 \text{ s}$

    $= 2500 \text{ m}$

2. (a) $T = \dfrac{D}{S}$

    $= \dfrac{400 \text{ m}}{2 \text{ m/s}}$

    $= 200 \text{ s}$

    (b) $T = \dfrac{2000 \text{ m}}{4 \text{ m/s}}$

    $= 500 \text{ s}$

3. (a) $S = \dfrac{D}{T}$

    $= \dfrac{300 \text{ m}}{12 \text{ s}}$

    $= 25 \text{ m/s}$

    (b) $S = \dfrac{1000 \text{ m}}{45 \text{ s}}$

    $= 22 \text{ m/s}$

4. (a) 18 minutes

    (b) After 10 minutes

    (c) 5 – 10 minutes (between B and C)

    (d) 11 – 15 minutes (between D and E)

    (e) 2km in 18 minutes $S = \dfrac{D}{T}$

    $= \dfrac{2000 \text{ m}}{18 \times 60 \text{ s}}$

    $= 1.9 \text{ m/s}$

Extension question

5.   (a)   **A graph to show the distance traveled by car**

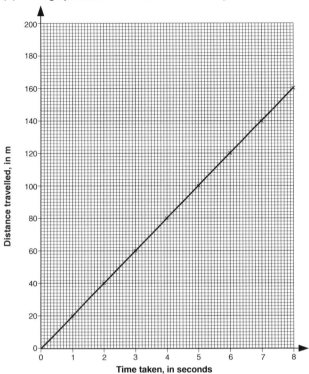

(b) $S = \dfrac{D}{T}$

$= \dfrac{160\,m}{8\,s}$

$= 20$ m/s

(c)   70m

(d)   140 − 80 = 60 m

(e)   D = S × T

= 20 m/s × 25 s

= 500 s

(f) $T = \dfrac{D}{S}$

$= \dfrac{400\,m}{20\,m/s}$

= 20 s

(g)   Along the level – it is moving at a constant speed of 20 m/s.

Exercise 26.3: Gravity

1. Weight is a force and is measured in **newtons**. It is caused by **gravity** acting on an object. ~~Weight~~ Mass is not a force, it depends on the number and **size** of particles in an object. Mass is measured in **grams** or **kg**.

2.

Mass in kg	Weight in newtons
2	20
1.5	15
3.7	37
5.5	55
9.2	92

3. There is less force of gravity between two apples than between the Earth and one apple because **gravity depends on the mass of the objects. The more massive the object, the bigger the gravitational force of attraction between them.**

Extension questions

4. (a)

Mass of added discs in grams	Position of spring in millimetres	Amount of stretch in millimetres
0	12	0
10	22	10
20	35	27
30	48	36
40	60	48
50	73	61
60	85	73
70	97	85
80	110	98
90	122	110
100	136	124
110	149	137
120	160	148

(b)

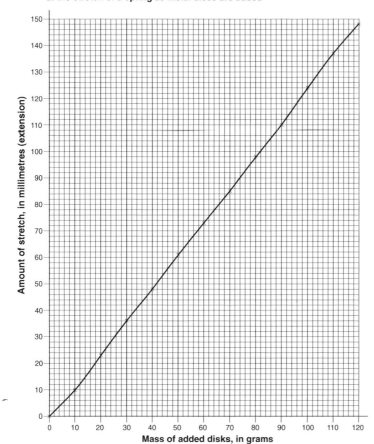

A graph to show the results of an experiment to look at the stretch of a spring as metal discs are added

(c) Greater mass leads to greater extension.

(d)

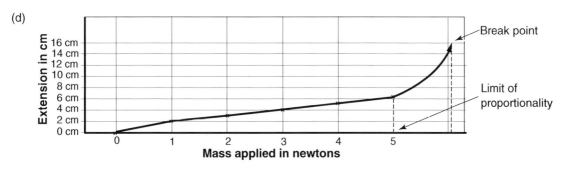

As the students keep on adding mass the spring would suddenly stretch much more than expected. The spring is stretched to breaking point and will not go back to its original length once the mass is removed. The elastic limits of the material would have been exceeded.

5. (a) 98 000 kilograms

(b) 980 000 newtons

(c) 980 000 newtons

Exercise 26.4: Balanced and unbalanced forces

1. Check pupils have drawn a car accelerating away from the traffic lights. Check they have drawn the force arrows to show the forces acting on the car.

2. A large lorry may have a more powerful engine than a racing car, but cannot accelerate so quickly because its **greater mass means that it has a greater 'downwards' force** so slowing it down.

Extension question

3. (a) 4 m/s/s

    (b) (i) 9 seconds: 36 m/s   (ii) 20 seconds: 80 m/s

    (c) Because of air resistance and frictional forces.

Chapter 27

Exercise 27.1: Friction

1.   Forces: – between brakes and wheel
                            – between tyres and road surface
                            – air resistance

2.   (a) True statement (i) Forward force and friction were both greater than zero.

     (b) 7 seconds

3.   When friction takes place, thermal energy is produced and surfaces are worn.

4.   Air resistance is the friction between a moving object and the air (sometimes called drag).

Extension questions

5.   (a) Changing: The type of test material.

     (b) Measuring: The force needed to move the trolley.

     (c) Constant: The surface and mass of trolley.

6.   (a)   **A graph to show the time taken to stop the motorbike, from the time when the accident was noticed**

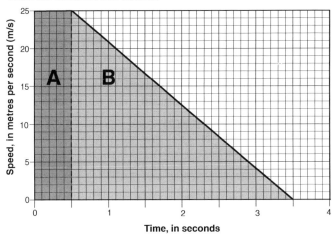

     (b) Total distance is the area under the graph e.g. A + B

          Area of A = 25 m/s × 0.5 s
                     = 12.5 m

          Area of B = 25 m/s × 1.5 s
                     = 37.5 m

          So total stopping distance = 37.5 m + 12.5 m
                                      = 50 m

     (c) The motorcyclist stops 20 m short of the accident

Exercise 27.2: Forces and rotation

1. (a) Y has the greater turning effect.
        This is because: for force Y 40 newtons × 0.2 metres = 8 newton metres
                        for force X 20 N × 0.3 m = 6 Nm

    (b) You could increase the turning effect of Y by increasing the distance between the applied force and the fulcrum / pivot.

2.

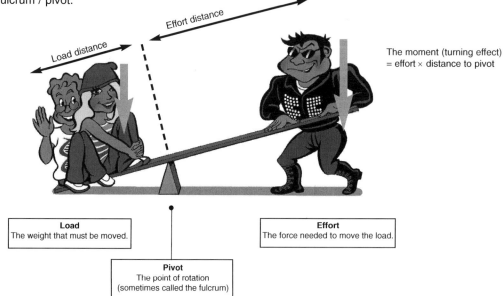

Load distance

Effort distance

The moment (turning effect) = effort × distance to pivot

Load
The weight that must be moved.

Effort
The force needed to move the load.

Pivot
The point of rotation
(sometimes called the fulcrum)

3. Formula for calculating a moment: **moment = force x distance to pivot**

    Forces are balanced when:

    the sum of the anti-clockwise moments = the sum of the clockwise moments

    force × distance (left-hand side) = force × distance (right-hand side)

Extension questions

4. Check pupils have identified the levers on the skeleton correctly.

5. (a) So that load does not cause it to topple over.

    (b) So that different loads can be balanced.

    (c) 4000 N × 6 m = 24 000 Nm

    (d) 24000 Nm

    (e) 2.4 m

    (f) 10 000 N × 2 m = x × 6 m

    $$x = \frac{10\,000 \text{ N} \times 2 \text{ m}}{6 \text{ m}}$$

    $$= 3333 \text{ N}$$

Exercise 27.3: Pressure

1. Units for pressure: Pascals (newtons/m²). For small areas (newtons/cm²)

   Formula: pressure = force/area

2. Woman's weight is 600 newtons.

   $F = P \times A$

   $\quad = 1200$ N/cm² $\times$ 0.5 cm²

   $\quad = 600$ N

3. (a) It is easier to walk on soft snow if you have snow shoes rather than ice skates because **the area is increased so that pressure falls and will no longer penetrate the snow**.

   (b) It is easier to pick up food with the prongs of a fork than with the handle because **the prongs have a small point (area is small) so that pressure is high for a small applied force.**

4. (a) 4 m²

   (b) $\dfrac{18000\,\text{N}}{4\text{m}^2} = 4500$ pascals or (4500 N/m²)

   (c) Area now equals 6 m² so pressure $= \dfrac{18000\,\text{N}}{6\,\text{m}^2} = 3000$ pascals Pa or N/m²

Extension question

5. (a) Check pupils have used the correct method for calculating how much pressure they put onto the surface of the Earth? Their answers should be given in newtons by measuring their mass (in kg) and multiplying by 10

   (b) Answer to the pressure exerted should be given in pascals, or N/m² or N/cm²

Chapter 28

Exercise 28.1: Light

1. You can't see an object unless there is some **light**. The objects you can see are either **luminous** (give out light) or **reflect** light into your eyes. Light is made up of **rays** and always travels in straight lines. A **shadow** is formed because light cannot pass through solid objects.

2. Light sources: **Sun, a torch, a burning candle**

3. Check for straight lines

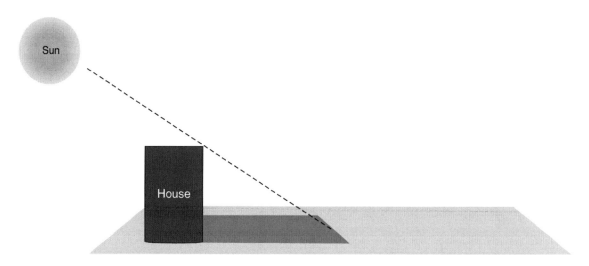

4. Examples could be: candle, match, torch, gas lamp, oil lamp

Extension questions

5. Show the reflection from the watch surface into the eyes of the viewer. Check the pupils' drawings for straight lines and that they have understood the principle that the angle of incidence equals the angle of reflection.

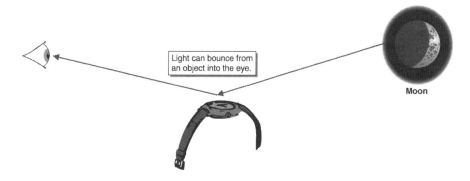

6. Check the pupils' drawings for straight lines. The cat can be seen in the shadow because some light reaches the cat and is reflected towards the viewer (shadow is not black).

7. Pupils' investigations into the measurement of the speed of light could include:

   – Galileo: Method 2 people, A and B took covered lanterns to the tops of hills separated by a mile. A uncovers the lantern and as soon as B sees A's light, he uncovers his. By measuring the time from when A uncovers the lantern until A sees B's light, then dividing this time by twice the distance between the hill top, the speed of light can be determined. However, the speed of light being what it is, and human reaction times being what they are, Galileo was able to determine only that the speed of light was far greater than could be measured using his procedure.

   – Romer (1675): Based his measurements on observations of the ellipses of one of the moons of Jupiter.

   – Fizeau: Used a rapidly revolving cogwheel in front of a light source to deliver the light to a distant mirror in discrete pulses.

   – Faucault: Improved Fizeau method, using a rotating mirror instead of a rotating cogwheel.

   – The fibre-optic method: Measures the time of flight of optical photons propagating along a fibre optic cable. Measurements are straightforward, with all timings being measured with an oscilloscope.

Exercise 28.2: Reflection

1. (i) Image – a reflection of an object in a mirror.

   (ii) Virtual – an image behind a mirror – it is not actually there.

   (iii) Inverted – upside down.

   (iv) Plane – flat.

   (v) Incidence – arrival of a light ray at the surface of a mirror.

2. Check the pupils have drawn the angles of reflection on the mirrors and that they have accurately drawn straight lines, and that they have included arrows to show light travelling from the object to the eye.

A PERISCOPE

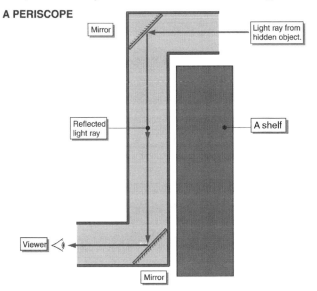

3. (a) 08.35 (20.35), 25 minutes to 9 o'clock.

    (b) Check pupils have written 08.35 backwards as it would be viewed in a mirror.

4. Check pupils have written their names and addresses (include the postcode) on a piece of paper so that it is the right way round in a mirror.

Extension questions

5. Many possible examples. A window against a darkened exterior would act like a mirror.

6. Check pupils' investigations into how optical cables are used in communications (including the advantages of using optical cables compared with copper cables).

Exercise 28.3: Refraction

1. Light is **refracted** when it reaches a boundary between two different substances. Each of the substances that light can pass through is called a **medium**. Light passing from a more dense to a **less** dense medium always bends **away from** the normal.

2. (a) It is hard to place your hand accurately on the coin because the rays are refracted. (Check pupils use of a diagram to help their explanation.)

    (b) It is hard to aim the spear accurately because the rays are refracted. (Check pupils use of a diagram to help their explanation.)

Extension question

3. Pupils should have found a diagram and made a simple drawing of a microscope. They should show how lenses direct the beam of light through the instrument.

Exercise 28.4: Colour

1. Anything suitable!

2. It would be very difficult to play snooker under a blue light because none of the colours (of the balls) would be reflected in blue light. A blue light absorbs all the colours except blue. The balls could not be distinguished.

3. (a) Red   (b) Black   (c) Red

4. So that they can be seen underwater. Underwater red light is filtered out so that a red wetsuit would appear black (and so be difficult to see).

5. Misha has a pair of special glasses, with coloured filters in place of normal lenses.

6. (a) This is because the green filter only allows green light to pass through it.

    (b) (i)   Red because red light can pass through the red filter.
         (ii) Black because the red light has no green to pass through the filter.

Chapter 29

Exercise 29.1: Sound

1.	Sounds are made when something **vibrates**. Vibrations then travel through the **air** to our ears. Vibrations can also travel through **liquids** (such as water) and **solids** (such as brick). Animals such as **dolphins/ whales/porpoises** are very good at hearing sounds underwater.

2.	When the first switch is closed, the bell sounds.

	When the second switch is closed and the pump is switched on, air is sucked out of the jar, creating a vacuum. This means that he sound of the bell gradually fades as the air is withdrawn because sound cannot travel through a vacuum.

3.	(a)	Light

	(b)	(iii) Sound cannot travel through a vacuum

Extension questions

4.	Check pupils' designs for an experiment to find out who has the most sensitive hearing in the group. They should write down what they would measure and explain how they would make certain that their experiment was a fair test.

5.	Pupils should have used a library book or the internet to explain how a hearing aid works.

Exercise 29.2: Pitch and loudness

1.	The distance between the tops of the waves on an oscilloscope trace is called the **wavelength**. The number of these that pass per second is called the **frequency** of the sound – it is measured in units called **hertz** and directly affects the **pitch** of a sound.

2.	Loosen the strings

3.	(a)	A loud sound with a high pitch: A

	(b)	A loud sound with a low pitch: B

	(c)	A quiet sound with a high pitch: C

	(d)	Two sounds with the same frequency: A and B or C and D

	(e)	Two sounds with the same amplitude: B and D or A and C

Extension questions

4. Objective: To check if the length of string affects the pitch of a sound that is made when the string is plucked

    Input variable: Length of string

    Output variable: Measure the frequency of the sound made by the plucking using an oscilloscope.

    Fair test/fixed variables: Thickness of string, effort used in plucking the string, distance of oscilloscope from string.

5. (a) **A graph to show the effects on the loudness of sound when dropping weights onto the floor.**

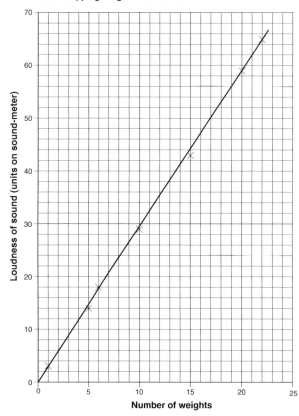

    (b) Increased number of weights (greater force) leads to increased loudness of sound.

    (c) 34 units

    (d) Freddie should have two sounds of equal frequency but different amplitude. More weights give greater amplitude.

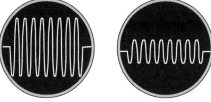

    Ten weights   Five weights

    (e) Drop them from the same height; weights made of same material; drop them onto same surface.

    (f) He could have improved the experiment by repeating the experiment and taking the mean of the results.